BIBLE TESTS

FASHIONED TO ACCOMPANY THE USE OF

Essentials of Bible History

By

ELMER W. K. MOULD, Ph.D.

ELMIRA COLLEGE

THE RONALD PRESS COMPANY · NEW YORK

2

PRINTED IN THE UNITED STATES OF AMERICA

PREFACE

During the twenty-four years in which these tests were being formulated, the author has used them with his classes. Where classes have been very large, the tests have served to keep students abreast of work assignments and to furnish the teacher with data for grading the students. Where classes have been small, the tests have proved most valuable in advancing student attainment; a few minutes at the beginning of class were devoted to the writing of the answers and part of the remainder of the period devoted to the correction of the papers by the students themselves. This correction process has never failed to lead into discussion of the implications of the questions and the background knowledge they call for, and students have had their errors straightened out before their minds got away from the subject.

The tests can be self-administered by students. Thereby they can check their understanding and mastery of the correlated parts of the textbook, the *Essentials of Bible History,* which these tests have been fashioned to accompany.

The author is indebted to his students through the years, on whom these tests have been inflicted, for their valuable criticisms and their help in the clearer formulation of statements. Especial gratitude is due Miss Marjorie Wilder for her valuable assistance, first as a student in the course using the quizzes, and then as the author's secretary in preparing the manuscript.

The tests are offered for wider use, not as being perfect, but in the hope that they may be of value. The suggested basis for computing scores follows the conventional percentage pattern. Other schemes of computation are possible and will be known to some teachers employing these tests in their classes.

On each test there is specified the number of the chapter in *Essentials of Bible History* with which it is correlated. Some of the tests cover only parts of chapters, and the section numbers of the parts of the chapters with which they are correlated are specified at the end of the tests on the Score line.

Elmer W. K. Mould

Elmira College
May 30, 1947

iii

CONTENTS

Arranged according to the sequence of chapters in the author's

Essentials of Bible History

MOULD BIBLE TESTS

i §§1–3, 5.

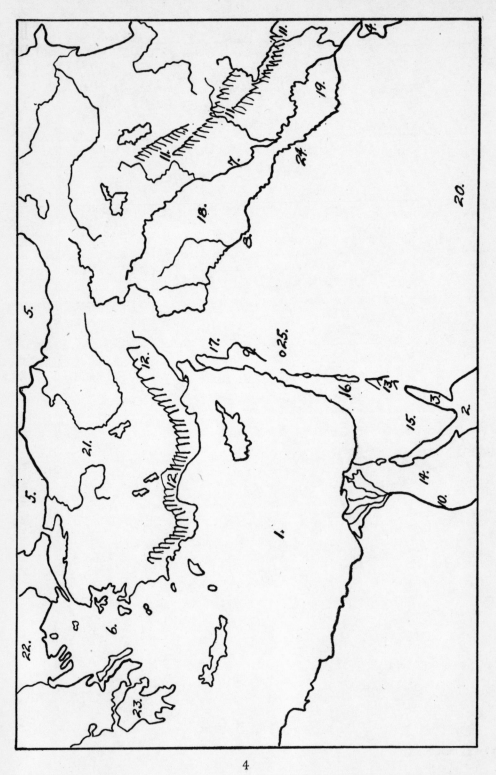

4

Identify the following:

BODIES OF WATER

1.......... 2.......... 3..........

4.......... 5.......... 6..........

RIVERS

7.......... 8.......... 9..........

10..........

MOUNTAINS

11.......... 12.......... 13..........

COUNTRIES

14.......... 15.......... 16..........

17.......... 18.......... 19..........

20.......... 21.......... 22..........

23..........

CITIES

24.......... 25..........

i §§1–3, 5. Number of items correctly stated = ... × 4 = Score..........

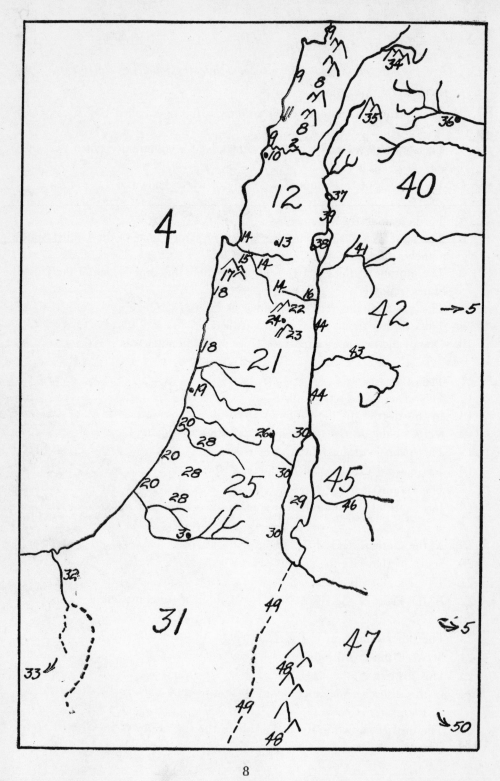

Give the information necessary to complete the following statements

1. This is an outline map of ....

2. The northern boundary of this country is the river called ....
   ....

3. The southern boundary of this country is at a community called ....
   ....

4. To the west of this country is a body of water known as ....
   ....

5. To the east of this country lies ....

6. The total area of this country is about the same as one of the United States,
   namely, ...

7. The latitude of this country is approximately the same as one of the United
   States, namely, ...

8. This mountainous region is known as ....

9. This country along the coast was called ....

10. One of the two most important cities in this country was ....
    ....

11. The other city was ....

12. This general district is called ....

13. In this district the most famous city was ....

14. South of the district named in item 12 lies the Plain of ....

15. This plain is drained by a river called ....

16. The eastern extension of this plain is the ....

17. This mountain is ....

18. Just south of this mountain is a plain along the coast called ....
    ....

19. At the southern end of this plain is the city of ....

20. South of that city the coastal plain is called ....

21. This general district is ....

22. In the heart of this district are two famous mountains; one is ....
    ....

23. The other mountain is ....

24. Between those two mountains lay the city of ....

25. This district is ....

26. In this district is the chief city of the entire land, namely the city of ......
    ....

27. The district named in item 25 is about the size of one of the United States,
    namely, ...

28. Between the district named in item 25 and the coastal plain named in item 20 is a lowland, or rolling country, called ....

29. This body of water is known as ....

30. Between this body of water and the district named in item 25 is a region known as ....

31. This region is known as the ....

32. In Bible times this stream was known as ....

33. If you go in this southwest direction you will come to the country known as
....

34. This mountainous ridge is known as ....

35. The southern extension of this ridge is Mount ....

36. The melting snows of these mountains form streams which water a rather extensive plain to the east, in the midst of which plain is a city known as the oldest city in the world, namely, ...

37. This little lake is known as ....

38. This lake is ....

39. The stream which connects these two lakes, flowing from 37 to 38, is ....
....

40. This district is called ....

41. The southern boundary of this district is the river ....

42. South of this river is the district called ....

43. The southern border of this district is the river called ....

44. The river which connects the lake named in item 38 with the body of water named in item 29 is ....

45. This district is called ....

46. This river is the ....

47. This region is called ....

48. It is a mountainous region, in a mountain ridge called Mount ....
....

49. West of this mountainous ridge is an area which lies below ocean level; it is called the ....

50. If you go in this southeast direction you will come to ....
....

Give the information necessary to complete the following statements.

1. In ancient Hebrew thought, the origin of nations was explained on the theory
that they were descendants of ....
The biblical account of this is in the book of ....
The ancient Hebrews seem to have regarded the peoples who inhabited the
Fertile Crescent and Arabia as the descendants of ....;
all peoples living to the north of the Fertile Crescent they regarded as the
descendants of ....; those in Egypt were considered
to be the descendants of ....
2. Sometimes the Hebrews are called Israelites, from Israel, a name first given
to ....; the name Israel means ....
....
3. The term Jew is derived from ....
4. The evidence of history is that the Semites originated in ....
................, from where they have for untold centuries spread fan-
wise into ....
5. By Semites is meant that part of the human race of which the ....
are perhaps the purest representatives today.
6. The term Aramean designates that minor division of the ....
peoples which, as far back as historical records go, was already long settled in .... and in ....
7. Some group names found in the Old Testament are perhaps authentic names
of the very earliest settlers in Palestine; five such names are
(1)...........................; (2)...........................;
(3)...........................; (4)...........................;
(5)...........................
8. The "Land of the Amorites" designates ....

ii §§1–2. Number of items adequately stated = ... × 5 = Score.........

*On the lines indicated by arrows insert the names of the peoples most promi-
nently identified with those areas in Bible times.*

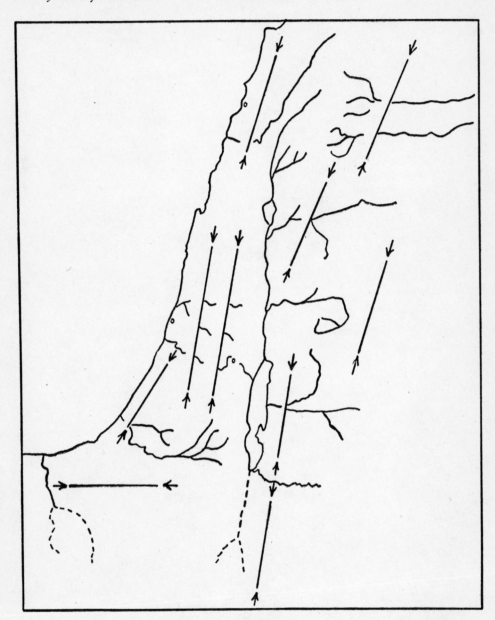

ii §§2–4. Number of items adequately stated =........ × 10 = Score........

*On the lines indicated by arrows insert the names of the peoples most promi-
nently identified with those areas in Bible times.*

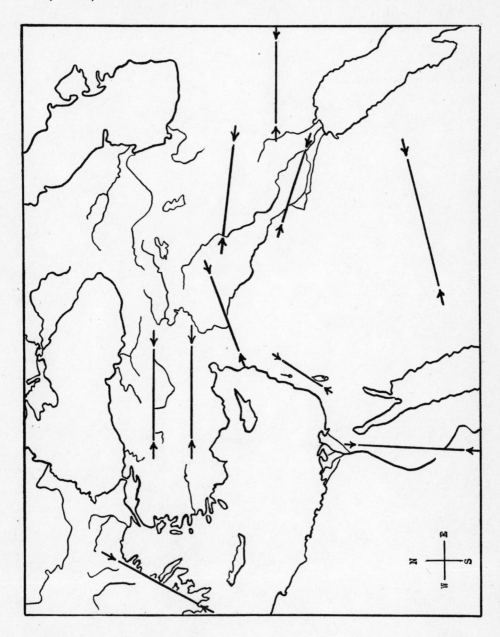

ii §§2–4. Number of items adequately stated = ... × 10 = Score........

For each archaeological monument give the information requested by writing the code number of an item in the appended list which correctly answers the question.

	Where discovered?		Where now found?	What significance for Bible study?
	country	locality		
Assuan Papyri.........				
Code of Hammurabi....				
Moabite Stone.........				
Siloam Inscription......				
Tell-el-Amarna Letters..				

1. Assyria
2. Babylon
3. Damascus
4. Dibon
5. Egypt
6. Elam
7. El-Amarna

8. Galilee
9. Gezer
10. Island of Elephantiné
11. Jerusalem
12. Karnak
13. Moab
14. Mouth of Nile River

15. Nazareth
16. Nineveh
17. Palestine
18. Persia
19. Susa
20. Syria
21. Thebes

22. British Museum in London
23. Field Museum, Chicago
24. Louvre in Paris
25. Metropolitan Museum of Art
26. Museum at Berlin, Germany
27. Museum at Cairo, Egypt
28. Museum at Istanbul, Turkey
29. Museum at Oxford, England
30. Oriental Institute, University of Chicago
31. Various Museums
32. Deciphering of cuneiform writing
33. Deciphering of hieroglyphic writing
34. Example of Old Semitic Script

35. Jews in Egypt in fifth century, B.C., that is, during Persian period
36. Light on enslavement of Hebrews in Egypt
37. Light on land of Canaan in fifteenth and fourteenth centuries, B.C.
38. Light on migrations of Hebrews in the Fertile Crescent
39. Light on reign of King Ahab of Israel
40. Light on reign of King Hezekiah of Judah
41. Raids of Habiri on Canaan
42. Social-historical basis of Mosaic laws in Old Testament

iii. Number of items correctly numbered = ... × 5 = Score..........

17

Check each item listed below in the appropriate column to indicate to which ancient civilization it properly pertains.

Cultural items	Babylo-nians	Canaan-ites	Egyp-tians	Philis-tines	Phoeni-cians
1. Abu Simbel Temple............					
2. Book of the Dead............					
3. Brick style of architecture.......					
4. Calendar of 365 days..........					
5. Code of Hammurabi...........					
6. Cuneiform writing					
7. Dissemination of alphabet.......					
8. Earliest attempt to establish religious monotheism					
9. Glazed-brick lion in Nebuchadrezzar's palace					
10. Great Hall of Karnak..........					
11. Hymn to Aton...............					
12. Lagash vase					
13. Maxims of Ptahhotep..........					
14. Political organization in nomes...					
15. Political organization under "five lords"					
16. Rameseum					
17. Ras Shamra tablets...........					
18. Recognition of banking and legal professions					
19. Sea-faring commerce					
20. 60-unit system of notation.......					
21. Tale of the Eloquent Peasant....					
22. Temple of Dagon.............					
23. Temple of Mekal at Bethshean....					
24. Writing on clay.............					
25. Ziggurat					

iv. Number of items correctly checked = ... × 4 = Score..........

19

Give the information necessary to complete the following statements.

1. The earliest era of Old Testament history is commonly designated as the
.... Era. It is so called because ....
....
....
This era covers a span of nearly ...... centuries, from about ...... B.C.
to about .... B.C. The Hebrews, during this era, were in the ....
.... stage of culture. The constituent unit of society was
.... The most characteristic feature of their experience during this era was ....
....

2. In this earliest era their chief occupation was ....

3. The expression, "going to their tents," literally means ....
....; figuratively it
means ....

4. Four articles included in the furnishings of a Hebrew home in the earliest
era were:
(1).........................; (2)...........................;
(3).........................; (4)...........................

5. Among the special tasks of the women in the earliest era were:
(1).........................; (2)...........................;
(3).........................; (4)...........................

6. The principal articles of diet in this earliest era were:
(1).........................; (2)...........................

7. Four outstanding personal traits which characterized the Hebrew of this
earliest era were:
(1).........................; (2)...........................;
(3).........................; (4)...........................

v §§1-2. Number of items adequately stated = ... × 4 = Score.........

Interpret the following story by appropriate comment on each numbered item.

"And <u>Yahweh</u> appeared unto him [<u>Abraham</u>] by the oaks of <u>Mamre</u>, as he

       1   2   3

sat in the <u>tent door</u> in the <u>heat of the day</u>; and he lifted up his eyes and looked,

          4   5

and, lo, <u>three men</u> stood near him; and when he saw them, he ran to meet them

      6

from the tent door, and <u>bowed himself to the ground</u> and said, <u>My lord</u>, if now

                            7   8

I have found favor in thy sight, pass not away, I pray thee, from thy servant;

let a little water be fetched, and <u>wash your feet,</u> and rest yourselves under the tree;

                                9

and I will fetch a morsel of <u>bread,</u> and refresh ye <u>your hearts</u>; after that ye shall

                 10   11

pass on. And they said, So do, as thou hast said. And Abraham hastened into

the tent unto <u>Sarah</u>, and said, Make ready quickly <u>three measures</u> of <u>fine meal</u>,

          12   13   14

knead it, and make <u>cakes.</u> And Abraham ran unto the herd, and fetched a calf

               15

tender and good, and gave it unto <u>a servant</u>; and he hasted to <u>dress it.</u> And he

                         16   17

took <u>butter,</u> and <u>milk,</u> and the calf which he had dressed, and set it before them;

     18   19

and he <u>stood by them</u> under the tree, and they did eat."

        20

v §1. **Number of items adequately interpreted** = ...× 5 = Score.........

Give the information necessary to complete the following statements.

1. The term "patriarch" means ....
2. The most eminent patriarchs were (1)..............................;
   (2).........................; (3)...........................
3. The earliest of the eminent patriarchs probably lived in the ....th
   century B.C. He settled in the land of ....
4. The most eminent patriarchs were eponymous heroes, which means ......
   ....
   ....
5. In this era wealth consisted in ....
6. Under the patriarchal form of government, the authority which the group
   recognized in social relations was ....
7. The stories about the patriarchs are in the Bible book of ....
   The purpose which seems to have determined the selection of stories included in this book was ....
   ....
8. In interpreting the text, "A nomad Aramean was my father; he went down
   to Egypt to reside there, with a small company, and there he became a
   nation," nomad means ....;
   Aramean means ....;
   the "father" was ....;
   the reason why he went down to Egypt was ....;
   his migration to Egypt took place either in the era of ....
   ...., or in the time of
   ....
9. Israel was ....
10. Joseph was the son of ....;
    he was famous because ....

v §§3–6. Number of items adequately stated = ... × 5 = Score.........

25

Indicate whether the following statements are true or false by underscoring the appropriate word. Correct any false statement on the blank line following it; the first half of any statement must be retained in any proposed correction.

1. The patriarchal era began / about 200 B.C.   TRUE FALSE 1
....

2. The patriarchal era covers a total of / eight centuries.   TRUE FALSE 2
....

3. The constituent unit in Hebrew society in the patriarchal era was / the individual person.   TRUE FALSE 3
....

4. In the patriarchal era the principal occupation of the Hebrews was / farming.   TRUE FALSE 4
....

5. The Hebrews, in the patriarchal era, dwelt in / tents.   TRUE FALSE 5
....

6. The principal article of diet in patriarchal times was / meat.   TRUE FALSE 6
....

7. The milk most commonly used in patriarchal times was / cow's milk.   TRUE FALSE 7
....

8. "Coat" and "cloak" were / different names for the same garment.   TRUE FALSE 8
....

9. In times of mourning the ancient Hebrews wore / sackcloth.   TRUE FALSE 9
....

10. A certain dry measure of capacity was called / the ephod.   TRUE FALSE 10
....

11. The migrations of Abraham were principally in / the Fertile Crescent.   TRUE FALSE 11
....

12. The place from which Abraham originally set out upon his migrations was / Ur.   TRUE FALSE 12
....

13. The Hebrews always thought of their twelve tribes as descended from / the twelve sons of Abraham.   TRUE FALSE 13
....

14. Keturah was / the daughter of Abraham.   TRUE   FALSE   14

....

15. Sodom was / an ancient king of the Jordan valley.   TRUE   FALSE   15

....

16. Stories about the Hebrew patriarch Isaac are in the book of / Genesis.   TRUE   FALSE   16

....

17. The South was / the Negeb.   TRUE   FALSE   17

....

18. Israel was the name of / Jacob.   TRUE   FALSE   18

....

19. Esau was / the brother of Jacob.   TRUE   FALSE   19

....

20. Rachel was / the sister of Jacob.   TRUE   FALSE   20

....

21. Seah was / the wife of Jacob.   TRUE   FALSE   21

....

22. Laban was / the father-in-law of Jacob.   TRUE   FALSE   22

....

23. Gomorrah was / a city in the Jordan plain destroyed by "brimstone and fire."   TRUE   FALSE   23

....

24. In the time of Joseph the Hebrews went down to Egypt because / they were taken captives by an Egyptian king who conquered Canaan.   TRUE   FALSE   24

....

25. In Egypt the Hebrews resided in / Goshen.   TRUE   FALSE   25

....

v. Number of statements correctly judged and adequately corrected = ...

$\times 4 =$ Score.........

Give the information necessary to complete the following statements.

1. Chapter VI of this course of study is entitled ....
   ....
   In this chapter our thought is oriented in that epoch of Old Testament his-
   tory known as ....
   Source material about this epoch may be found in the biblical books of
   ....
   The approximate date of the beginning of this epoch is .... B.C.,
   at which time occurred the event known as ....

2. At the beginning of this chapter of our course, the life and experiences of the
   Hebrews are intimately related to the empire of ....,
   and particularly to the ruler of that empire named ....
   The attitude of that ruler toward the Hebrews led him to take the following
   specific actions with respect to them: (1).............................
   ....,
   (2)...
   ....
   The immediate effect of this treatment upon the social status of the Hebrews
   was to ....

3. Goshen was ....
   ....

4. Pithom was ....
   ....

5. The pharaoh in whose time the Hebrew tribesmen under Moses left Egypt
   was probably ....

6. The last of the plagues of Egypt was ....
   ....

7. "The Way of the Wilderness" was a route that led from ....
   .... to ....

8. The Yâm Sûph means (translated) ....
   and designates ....

vi §§1–5.   **Number of items adequately stated** = ... × 5 = Score.........

Number each item in the second column to correspond with that word in the first column with which it is correctly associated.

1. Aaron	( ) Attempted a rebellion against Moses in the wilderness
2. Akabah	( ) Brother of Moses
3. Arabah	
4. Ark	( ) Central rendezvous of the Hebrews in the wilderness
5. Arnon	( ) Companion of Moses during battle of Hebrews with
6. Baalim	Amalekites
7. Balaam	
8. Balak	( ) Country which the Hebrews were forbidden to cross
9. Barak	( ) King of Bashan
10. Caleb	( ) King of the Amorites
11. Covenant	( ) King of Moab who sought to expel the Hebrews
12. Decalogue	
13. Deuteronomy	( ) Moses' father-in-law
14. Edom	( ) Most probable pharaoh of the Exodus
15. Elath	( ) Mountain from which Moses viewed the Promised Land
16. Goshen	( ) Mountain where Moses received the Ten Command-
17. Hor	ments
18. Horeb	
19. Hur	( ) Name of a wilderness
20. Jethro	( ) One of the twelve spies who advised going into Canaan
21. Joseph	from the South
22. Kadesh	
23. Korah	( ) Soothsayer hired to curse the Hebrews
24. Levi	( ) Store city in Egypt
25. Merneptah	( ) The Ten Commandments
26. Midian	
27. Nebo	( ) Tribe to which Moses belonged
28. Negeb	( ) What the Bible calls the "Red Sea"
29. Numbers	( ) Where Moses was a shepherd
30. Og	
31. Paran	
32. Passover	
33. Pithom	
34. Raamses	
35. Seir	
36. Shur	
37. Sihon	
38. Sin	
39. Yâm Sûph	
40. Zin	

vi. Number of items correctly numbered = ... ✕ 5 = Score..........

31

Interpret the following story by appropriate comment on each numbered item.

"And <u>Yahweh</u> spake unto <u>Moses,</u> saying, Send thou men, that they may
₁   ₂

search out the <u>land of Canaan,</u> which I give unto <u>the children of Israel;</u> of every
           ₃   ₄

tribe of their fathers shall ye send a man, every one a leading man among them.
₅

And Moses sent them from the <u>wilderness of Paran</u> according to Yahweh's
                                 ₆

commandment . . . and said unto them, Get you up by way of the <u>South,</u> and
                                                    ₇

go into <u>the hill-country;</u> and see the land, what it is; and the people that dwell
          ₈

there, whether they are strong or weak, few or many; and what the land is

that they dwell in, whether it is good or bad; and what the cities are like that

they dwell in, whether camps, or strongholds; and what the land is, whether fat

or lean, whether there is wood in it, or not. And be ye of good courage, and

bring of the fruit of the land. Now the time was <u>the time of the first-ripe grapes.</u>
                                                         ₉

So they went up and searched out the land from the <u>wilderness of Zin</u> unto
                                              ₁₀

Rehob, at the <u>entrance to Hamath.</u> And they went up by way of the South,
           ₁₁

and came unto <u>Hebron.</u> . . . They came to the valley of Eshcol, where they
          ₁₂

cut down a branch with one cluster of grapes, and they carried it between two

upon a staff; they brought also some pomegranates, and figs. . . . And they

returned from searching out the land after forty days. And they went and came

to Moses, and to <u>Aaron,</u> and to all the congregation of the children of Israel,
         ₁₃

unto the wilderness of Paran, to <u>Kadesh.</u> . . . And they told him, and said, We
                       ₁₄

came unto the land whither thou sentest us; and surely it floweth with milk and

honey; and this is the fruit of it. But the people that inhabit the land are strong,

and the cities are walled and very large; moreover we saw the <u>children of Anak</u>
                                                         ₁₅

there. <u>Amalek</u> inhabits the land of the South; and the <u>Hittite,</u> and the <u>Jebusite,</u>
     ₁₆   ₁₇   ₁₈

and the Amorite inhabit the hill-country; and the Canaanite dwells by the sea,
and along the Jordan. And Caleb stilled the people before Moses, and said, Let
us go up at once, and possess it; for we are well able to overcome it. But the
men that went up with him said, We are not able to go up against the people;
for they are stronger than we."

vi. Number of items adequately interpreted = ... $\times$ 5 = Score.........

The following statements are arranged alphabetically according to their initial words. Arrange them chronologically *according to the sequence in which they occur in the biblical narrative or fit into the history of the times. Numbers 1, 2, and 3 are marked as samples.* Continue the numbering to indicate the sequence. *To facilitate the work the statements have been reprinted on Sheet 2, from which they may be detached for sorting.*

(...) Aaron makes a golden calf for the Israelites to worship
(...) Balak, king of Moab, tries to get Balaam to curse the Israelites
(...) Egyptian militia destroyed at the "Sea of Reeds" [=Yâm Sûph]
(...) Hebrew laborers help build the city of Pithom in Egypt
(...) Hebrew scouts survey Canaan to determine the feasibility of a Hebrew invasion of Canaan via the Negeb
(...) Hebrew tribesmen under the leadership of Korah rebel against Moses' leadership at Kadesh
(...) Hebrews defeat Sihon, king of the Amorites
(...) Hebrews engage in a successful battle with Amalekites
(...) Hyksos gain control of Egypt
(...) Ikhnaton becomes pharaoh of Egypt
(3) Jacob dreams of God at Bethel
(...) King of Edom refuses to permit Israelites to cross his territory
(...) Merneptah becomes pharaoh of Egypt
(...) Moses murders Egyptian slave-gang foreman
(...) Moses surveys the Promised Land from Mount Nebo
(...) Moses works as a shepherd in Midian
(...) Plagues visited upon Egypt
(...) Ramses II becomes pharaoh of Egypt
(2) Rebekah marries Isaac
(1) Sodom and Gomorrah are destroyed
(...) The Ethical Decalogue is formulated
(...) The Israelites construct a sacred chest to symbolize the presence of their god with them
(...) The Israelites reach Mount Sinai

For each item numbered to follow its correct predecessor,   score 5
For an item numbered out of sequence by not more than one place,   score 4
For an item numbered out of sequence by not more than two places, score 3

vi.   Total score = ...

(*Continued on Sheet 2*)

Detach and sort the items chronologically.

(...) Aaron makes a golden calf for the Israelites to worship	(...) Balak, king of Moab, tries to get Balaam to curse the Israelites
(...) Egyptian militia destroyed at the "Sea of Reeds" [=Yâm Sûph]	(...) Hebrew laborers help build the city of Pithom in Egypt
(...) Hebrew scouts survey Canaan to determine the feasibility of a Hebrew invasion of Canaan via the Negeb	(...) Hebrew tribesmen under the leadership of Korah rebel against Moses' leadership at Kadesh
(...) Hebrews defeat Sihon, king of the Amorites	(...) Hebrews engage in a successful battle with Amalekites
(...) Hyksos gain control of Egypt	(...) Ikhnaton becomes pharaoh of Egypt
(...) King of Edom refuses to permit Israelites to cross his territory	(...) Merneptah becomes pharaoh of Egypt
(...) Moses murders Egyptian slave-gang foreman	(...) Moses surveys the Promised Land from Mount Nebo
(...) Moses works as a shepherd in Midian	(...) Plagues visited upon Egypt
(...) Ramses II becomes pharaoh of Egypt	(...) The Ethical Decalogue is formulated
(...) The Israelites construct a sacred chest to symbolize the presence of their god with them	(...) The Israelites reach Mount Sinai

Give the information necessary to complete the following statements.

1. Parallelism means ....
....
2. The unit of parallelism is ....
3. A suitable title for the following is

....

Spring up, O well;
Sing ye unto it;
Well, which princes digged,
Which nobles delved,
With the sceptre,
And with their staffs.

Lines 3 and 4 of the foregoing illustrate .... parallelism.

4. A suitable title for the following is

....

Adah and Zillah, hear my voice,
Wives of Lamech, attend to my word;
For I kill a man for a wound to me
And a boy for a scar.
For Cain takes vengeance seven times,
But Lamech seventy times seven.

Lines 3 and 4 of the foregoing illustrate .... parallelism.

5.   "I will sing unto the LORD, for he hath triumphed gloriously;
            The horse and his rider hath he thrown into the sea."

The above is an example of .... parallelism,
the distinguishing feature of which is ....
....

6.   "Cursed be every one that curseth thee,
            And blessed be he that blesseth thee."

The above is an example of .... parallelism,
the distinguishing feature of which is ....
....

vii. Number of items adequately stated = ... × 10 = Score..........

39

Give the information necessary to complete the following statements.

1. Five important aspects of religion are:
   (1) ....
   (2) ....
   (3) ....
   (4) ....
   (5) ....
2. In Old Testament religion are to be found the genetic connections of three of the world's now living religions, namely:
   (1)................... (2).................. (3)...............
3. The story of Old Testament religion is the story of a long development. It begins with ....
   .... and culminates in ....
   ....
4. Theophany means ....
   ....
5. The principal festivals connected with nomad religious worship were
   (1)........................... (2)...........................
   (3)........................... (4)...........................
6. The Hebrew name Kadesh means .... and designates
   ....
7. The Blood Covenant was based upon the idea that.....................
   ....
   The act by which it was carried out was ....
   ....
8. The Old Testament term *"unclean"* is a technical term which means ......
   ....
   ....

Interpret the following story by appropriate comment on each numbered item.

"Now <u>Moses</u> was tending the flock of Jethro his father-in-law, the <u>priest</u>
₁   2

of <u>Midian</u>; and he led the flock to <u>the farthest side of the desert,</u> and came <u>to</u>
 2   3   4

the <u>mountain of God,</u> Horeb. And the <u>angel of Yahweh</u> appeared unto him in
    4   5

a <u>flame of fire</u> out of the midst of a bush; and he looked, and, behold, the bush
  6

burned with fire, and <u>the bush was not consumed.</u> And Moses said, I will turn
                             7

aside and see this great sight, why the bush is not burnt. And when Yahweh

saw that he turned aside to see, God called unto him out of the midst of the bush,

and said, Moses, Moses. And he said, Here am I. And he said, Draw not nigh

hither; <u>put off thy shoes</u> from off thy feet, for the place whereon thou standest
     8

is <u>holy ground.</u> Moreover he said, I am the God of <u>Abraham,</u> the God of <u>Isaac,</u>
  9   10   11

and the God of <u>Jacob.</u> And Moses hid his face, for he was <u>afraid to look upon</u>
         12   13

<u>God.</u> And Yahweh said, I have surely seen the affliction of <u>my people that are in</u>
 13   14

<u>Egypt,</u> and have heard their cry by reason of their taskmasters; for I know their
 14

sorrows; and I am come down to deliver them out of the hand of the Egyptians,

and to bring them up out of that land unto a good land and a large, unto a

land flowing with <u>milk and honey;</u> unto the place of the <u>Canaanites,</u> and the
                15   16

<u>Hittites,</u> and the <u>Amorites,</u> and the <u>Perizzites,</u> and the <u>Hivites,</u> and the <u>Jebusites.</u>
 17   18   19   20   21

Behold, the cry of the children of Israel is come unto me. I have seen <u>the oppres-</u>
                                                      22

<u>sion wherewith the Egyptians oppress them.</u> Come now therefore, and <u>I will</u>
             22   23

<u>send thee</u> unto Pharaoh, that thou mayest bring forth my people the children of
 23

Israel out of Egypt. And Moses said unto God, Who am I, that I should go unto

<u>Pharaoh,</u> and that I should bring forth the children of Israel out of Egypt? And
 24

he said, Certainly I will be with thee; and this shall be the token unto thee, that

43

I have sent thee; when thou hast brought forth the people out of Egypt, ye shall

serve God upon this mountain."

25. The time setting of the foregoing narrative is . . . .

. . . .

Give the information necessary to complete the following statements.

1. Henotheism means ....,......................
   ....
   It is to be differentiated from monotheism, which means ....
   ....

2. Yahwism is ....
   ....

3. Of all the sacred mountains mentioned in the Old Testament, the most important is .... because ....
   ....

4. The Ark of the Covenant was ....
   .... It may have contained ....
   .... The Covenant was
   ....

5. The Tent of Meeting was ....
   It was so called because ....

6. The preëminent Hebrew religious festival has always been ....
   It commemorates ....
   ....

7. The expression, "to inquire of Yahweh," means ....
   ....

8. Urim and Thummim were ....
   ....

9. The ephod was ....
   ....

10. Notable among the virtues which characterized the nomadic Hebrews were
    (1)...
    (2)...
    (3)...
    (4)...
    (5)...

Interpret the following passages in such a way as to point out clearly the historical problem involved and suggest a solution of the problem. One aspect of the problem is presented in passage (1), and another aspect of the problem is presented in passages (2), (3), and (4).

I

(1) "And God spake unto Moses, and said unto him, I am Yahweh; and I appeared unto Abraham, unto Isaac, and unto Jacob, as God Almighty [El Shaddai]; but by my name Yahweh I was not known to them." (Ex. 6:2–3)

II

(2) "And he [Abraham] believed in Yahweh; and he [Yahweh] counted it to him [Abraham] for righteousness. And he said unto him, I am Yahweh that brought thee out of Ur of the Chaldees, to give thee this land to inherit it. And he [Abraham] said, O Lord Yahweh, whereby shall I know that I shall inherit it?" (Gen. 15:6–8)

(3) "And he [Isaac] went up thence to Beersheba. And Yahweh appeared unto him the same night, and said, I am the God of Abraham thy father; fear not, for I am with thee, and will bless thee, and multiply thy seed for my servant Abraham's sake. And he builded an altar there, and called upon the name of Yahweh." (Gen. 26:23–25)

(4) In the story of Jacob's dream it is stated: "Yahweh stood above it [the ladder], and said, I am Yahweh, the God of Abraham thy father, and the God of Isaac. . . . And Jacob awaked out of his sleep, and he said, Surely Yahweh is in this place; and I knew it not." (Gen. 28:13, 16)

Number each item in the second column to correspond with that word in the first column with which it is correctly associated.

1. Ark
2. Azazel
3. Berîth
4. Bethel
5. Bethshemesh
6. Chemosh
7. Cromelech
8. Decalogue
9. Dolmen
10. Elôhîm
11. El roi
12. El Shaddai
13. 'En-mishpat
14. Ephod
15. Gilgal
16. Henotheism
17. Horeb
18. Hydromancy
19. Kadesh
20. Machpelah
21. Mamre
22. Mazzebah
23. Midian
24. Molech
25. Monotheism
26. Necromancy
27. Pesach
28. Seraphim
29. Se'irim
30. Sin
31. Sinai
32. Taboo
33. Tent of Meeting
34. Teraphim
35. Terebinth
36. Theophany
37. Thummim
38. Unclean
39. Urim
40. Yahwism

( ) Appearance and revelation of the deity, who is both seen and heard

( ) "Burning Ones"; a type of supernatural beings

( ) Chief demon of the wilderness

( ) Divination by conjuring up the shades of the dead

( ) Exclusive worship of a particular god, though not denying the existence of other deities

( ) "God Almighty"; an early Hebrew name for their deity

( ) Hebrew word, technical term for an upright stone shaft which marks a sacred place

( ) Hebrew word, technical term meaning covenant

( ) Household gods

( ) Most important of all sacred mountains

( ) Objects used in casting the sacred lot

( ) Old Testament technical term for things forbidden

( ) Preëminent Hebrew religious festival

( ) Preëminent Hebrew sanctuary during the wilderness period

( ) Preferred Old Testament (Hebrew) word for God

( ) Sacred chest which symbolized the Hebrew deity's immediate presence

( ) "Stone Circle"; an Old Testament place name

( ) Technical name for the Hebrew religion founded by Moses

( ) Ten Commandments

( ) Tree of the type usually associated with a sacred place.

Give the information necessary to complete the following statements.

1. Chapter IX of this course of study is entitled ....

   ....

   In this chapter our thought is oriented in that epoch of Old Testament history known as ....

2. Moses' immediate successor as leader of the Hebrew tribes was ....

   ...., who became leader approximately .... B.C. This man's name means ....

3. Certain Hebrew tribes, namely, ...

   ....

   settled permanently east of Jordan; they settled in territory taken from

   ....

4. After the Hebrews crossed the Jordan, they established their camp at

   ....

5. For invading forces from east of Jordan, the key city to the west Jordan territory was ...., because ....

   ....

   The story of the capture of this city is found in the biblical book of ....

   ....

6. The west Jordan region was occupied by the Hebrew tribes in [how many?] .... distinct areas, each separated from the others by ....

   ....

   In each of these areas the leading tribe was ....

   ....

   ....

7. It is important to bear in mind the cultural contrast between the Canaanites and the Hebrews. The Canaanites were ....

   .... The Hebrews were

   ....

8. Four important reasons why the Hebrews could successfully enter and settle Canaan, despite the fact that the Canaanites already possessed the land, were

   (1)..

   ....;

(2)...
....;
(3)...
....;
(4)...
....

ix §§1–6. Number of items adequately stated = ... × 4 = Score........

Give the information necessary to complete the following statements.

1. "Wrought stone" was ....
2. The roof of a Palestinian house was put to a variety of uses, including
   (1)............................ (2)............................
   (3)............................
3. An "upper room" was ....
4. "Ivoried houses" were ....
5. "Earthen vessels" were ....
6. A "kneading trough" was ....
7. "Fleshhooks" were ....
8. The "staff of life" was ....
9. "Trees for food" were ....
10. The "fruit of the vine" was ....
11. The "former rain" was ....
12. The "latter rain" was ....
13. A "threshing floor" was ....
14. Winnowing means ....
15. A "fan" was ....
16. Two factors which determined the location of communities were
    (1)............................ (2)............................
17. The "sheep gate" was ....
18. The "fuller's field" was ....
19. A "high place" was ....
20. "Broad places" were ....
21. The "strong tower" was ....
22. "Elders" were ....

ix §11. Number of items adequately stated = ... $\times$ 4 = Score........

Indicate whether the following statements are true or false by underscoring the appropriate word. Correct any false statement on the blank line following it; the first half of any statement must be retained in any proposed correction.

1. The story of the conquest and settlement of Canaan is recorded in / the book of Numbers.   TRUE   FALSE   1
....

2. The Hebrews were obliged to capture Jericho / before they could cross the Jordan to enter Canaan.   TRUE   FALSE   2
....

3. Moses died / just after he had successfully led the Hebrews across the Jordan river.   TRUE   FALSE   3
....

4. The central camp of the Hebrews after crossing the Jordan was / at Gilgal.   TRUE   FALSE   4
....

5. The Hebrews entered Canaan for the definitive conquest / about 1150 B.C.   TRUE   FALSE   5
....

6. The definitive conquest and settlement of Canaan by the Hebrews took / forty years.   TRUE   FALSE   6
....

7. The tribes of Reuben and Gad / assisted in the conquest of West-Jordan Canaan.   TRUE   FALSE   7
....

8. The fact that Canaan was a country of little cities and towns, very independent and usually hostile to one another, made it / difficult for the Hebrews to gain a foothold in the land.   TRUE   FALSE   8
....

9. Deborah was / the wife of Joshua.   TRUE   FALSE   9
....

10. The "Judges" were / magistrates appointed by Joshua to preside over the courts of the Hebrews.   TRUE   FALSE   10
....

11. The period of the "Judges" witnessed the transformation of the Hebrews / from an agricultural to a pastoral people.   TRUE   FALSE   11
....

12. Sisera was / commander-in-chief of the coalition of Canaanites against the Hebrews.　　　TRUE　FALSE　12

. . . .

13. Barak was commander of the army of / the Hebrews in their battle against the Canaanites.　　　TRUE　FALSE　13

. . . .

14. The Hebrews / ultimately exterminated the Canaanites.　　　TRUE　FALSE　14

. . . .

15. Gideon and his followers suppressed the raids of / the Phoenicians.　　　TRUE　FALSE　15

. . . .

16. Jerubaal was / the son of Gideon.　　　TRUE　FALSE　16

. . . .

17. The opposition of the Ammonites east of Jordan was ended by the Hebrews under the leadership of / Jephthah.　　　TRUE　FALSE　17

. . . .

18. An average Hebrew home was / one story high.　　　TRUE　FALSE　18

. . . .

19. The most fertile farming districts were in / Judea.　　　TRUE　FALSE　19

. . . .

20. Hebrew farmers lived / in isolated farm houses scattered over the countryside.　　　TRUE　FALSE　20

. . . .

21. For Hebrew farmers and laborers the principal meal of the day was / at noon.　　　TRUE　FALSE　21

. . . .

22. The stories of Ruth and the boy Samuel reflect / the cruelty and rudeness of the age of the "Judges."　　　TRUE　FALSE　22

. . . .

23. At the close of the period of the "Judges" the only remaining aggressive enemies of the Hebrews were / the Philistines.　　　TRUE　FALSE　23

. . . .

24. The Philistines came from / Crete.　　　TRUE　FALSE　24

. . . .

25. The Philistines settled in / the plain of Esdraelon.　　　TRUE　FALSE　25

. . . .

ix §§7–12. Number of statements correctly judged and adequately corrected =

. . . . × 4 = Score . . . .

Give the information necessary to complete the following account of

THE CONQUEST OF CANAAN

The Canaanites did not hinder the Hebrews' penetration of their country for three principal reasons:

(1)...

....

(2)...

....

(3)...

....

The time came, however, when the Canaanites organized their forces to repress the Hebrews. Their opposition came to a climax in the famous battle of ......

.... The center of the Canaanite confederacy was

........................, a walled town. Under the fiery exhortation of the

prophetess .... a Hebrew army was recruited from five of the Hebrew tribes, namely, (1)..

(2).............................. (3)..............................

(4).............................. (5)..............................

The Canaanites had the advantage over the Hebrews in military equipment. The Canaanite military leader was .... The Hebrew military leader, named, ..., offset this Canaanite advantage by

....

....

Hebrew morale was high because ....

....

A factor which specially contributed to the Hebrew victory was ....

....

The Canaanite military chieftain met an ignominious death, in that ....

....

After this battle there was peace between Canaanites and Hebrews. Ultimately the Canaanites disappeared from history because ....

....

The Hebrews, in central Canaan, also had to contend with marauding bands of Midianites and Amalekites. So serious did this marauding become that one Hebrew, named ...., was compelled to ....

....

He thereupon rallied his fellow tribesmen of the tribe of ....

and also men from the tribes of (1)..

(2).......................... and (3)..........................

to resistance. Fired by the war cry, "..............................
....,"
they drove the Midianites ....
.... and ended the menace.

The Hebrews made Eastjordania secure by suppressing three enemies there.
The Hebrew "judge" Othniel expelled the ....
Ehud freed the Hebrews from raids by ....
The aggression of the Ammonites was checked by ....
In connection with this last-named "judge's" victory occurred a tragedy in his
own family, namely, ...
....

The most difficult of all enemies for the Hebrews to suppress were the
.... These people originally came from ....
They made an unsuccessful attempt to invade ...., after which
they invaded Palestine at about the same time the Hebrews did, which was
....
In Palestine they settled principally in the area of ....
where they dispossessed the .... These people set about
to subjugate all Palestine. Two of the Hebrew "judges" clashed ineffectively
with them, namely, (1).................... and (2)....................
It became evident that only the total union of all Hebrew tribes under a king
could meet this menace. In choosing a king, the Hebrews were guided by the
prophet ...., who anointed .... as king.
This man's kingdom by no means covered all the tribes; it centered in the tribe
of .... and included only (1)........................
(2)......................... and (3).........................,
so that he really was more of a "judge" than a king. The principal accomplishments of his reign were (1)...
....
(2)...
(3)...
He failed to achieve two very important objectives, namely, (1)..............
....
(2)...
These objectives were later achieved by .... after which
the Hebrews were in secure possession of Palestine as their homeland.

ix. Number of items adequately stated = ... ✕ 2 = Score...........

58

Indicate whether the following statements are true or false by underscoring the appropriate word. Correct any false statement on the blank line following it; the first half of any statement must be retained in any proposed correction.

1. Harvest and vintage festivals were part of the worship of Yahweh during / the wilderness period.　　TRUE　FALSE　1
   ....

2. When they first settled among the Canaanites, the Hebrews were / strict monotheists.　　TRUE　FALSE　2
   ....

3. During the era of the settlement in Canaan, Hebrew religion was predominantly / ethical in character.　　TRUE　FALSE　3
   ....

4. During the period of the conquest of Canaan, Yahweh was thought of as / a god of nature.　　TRUE　FALSE　4
   ....

5. The Book of the Wars of Yahweh is / one of the books of the Hebrew Holy Scriptures.　　TRUE　FALSE　5
   ....

6. "Ingathering" was / the military muster of the Hebrew army.　　TRUE　FALSE　6
   ....

7. The Ark and the Tent of Meeting reminded the Hebrews, in their journeys, of / their deity, Yahweh, who was far away on Mt. Horeb.　　TRUE　FALSE　7
   ....

8. After the Hebrews entered Canaan, the Ark was located / at Jerusalem in the temple.　　TRUE　FALSE　8
   ....

9. "To the help of Yahweh" was the rallying cry of / Deborah the prophetess.　　TRUE　FALSE　9
   ....

10. Malik was / a military leader who coöperated with Deborah.　　TRUE　FALSE　10
    ....

11. Shiloh was / the priest in charge of the Ark.　　TRUE　FALSE　11
    ....

12. An ephod was / a type of waistcoat worn by priests.　　TRUE　FALSE　12
    ....

13. The Canaanites worshiped / many baals.　　TRUE　FALSE　13
    ....

14. The word "baal" means / "owner."   TRUE   FALSE   14
    ....

15. Asherah was / the mother-goddess.   TRUE   FALSE   15
    ....

16. Ashtoreth was worshipped by / Canaanites.   TRUE   FALSE   16
    ....

17. "Houses of high places" were / rooms connected with
    village sanctuaries.   TRUE   FALSE   17
    ....

18. Mazzebah was / a Hebrew prophetess.   TRUE   FALSE   18
    ....

19. Worshiping Baal as well as Yahweh was / apostasy.   TRUE   FALSE   19
    ....

20. Samuel was / a prophet.   TRUE   FALSE   20
    ....

21. The Hebrew monarchy was initiated by / a prophet
    of Yahweh.   TRUE   FALSE   21
    ....

22. "Sons of the prophets" were / men whose fathers had
    been prophets.   TRUE   FALSE   22
    ....

23. Prophesying in Israel in the time of Samuel was char-
    acterized by / ecstatic elements.   TRUE   FALSE   23
    ....

24. Mana is / the name of the special food divinely pro-
    vided for the Hebrews in their wilderness wandering.   TRUE   FALSE   24
    ....

25. In later Hebrew usage, the word prophet meant / a
    spokesman.   TRUE   FALSE   25
    ....

x. Number of statements correctly judged and adequately corrected = ... ×
    4 = Score........

Interpret the following story by appropriate comment on each numbered item.

"Now Israel went out against <u>the Philistines</u> to battle, and camped beside
₁

Eben-ezer; and the Philistines camped in Aphek. And the Philistines put them-

selves in array against Israel; and when they joined battle, Israel was smitten

before the Philistines; and they slew of the army in the field about four thousand

men. And when the people were come into the camp, the <u>elders of Israel</u> said,
2

Wherefore hath <u>Yahweh</u> smitten us today before the Philistines? Let us fetch
3

the <u>ark</u> of the <u>covenant</u> of Yahweh out of Shiloh unto us, that when it cometh
4   5

among us, it may <u>save us</u> out of the hand of our enemies. So the people sent to
6

Shiloh, and brought from there the ark of the covenant of Yahweh of hosts, who

<u>sitteth upon the cherubim</u>; and the two sons of <u>Eli</u>, Hophni and Phineas, were
7   8

there with the ark of the covenant of God.

"And when the ark of the covenant of Yahweh came into the camp, all

Israel shouted with a great shout, so that the earth rang again. And when the

Philistines heard the noise of the shout, they said, What meaneth the noise of this

great shout in the camp of the Hebrews? And they understood that the ark of

Yahweh was come into camp. And the Philistines were afraid, for they said,

<u>God is come into the camp.</u> And they said, Woe unto us! for there hath not been
9

such a thing heretofore. Woe unto us! who shall deliver us out of the hand of

these <u>mighty gods</u>? these are the <u>gods</u> that smote the Egyptians with all the
10

plagues in the wilderness. Be strong, and quit yourselves like men, O ye Philis-

tines, that ye be not servants unto the Hebrews, <u>as they have been to you</u>; quit
11

yourselves like men, and fight. And the Philistines fought, and Israel was smit-

ten, and every man fled to his tent; and there was a very great slaughter; for there fell of Israel thirty thousand footmen. And the ark of God was taken; and the two sons of Eli, Hophni and Phineas, were slain. . . .

"Now the Philistines took the ark of God, and brought it from Eben-ezer unto Ashdod, into the house of Dagon, and set it by Dagon. And when they
  12   13
of Ashdod arose early on the morrow, behold, Dagon was fallen upon his face to the earth before the ark of Yahweh. And they took Dagon, and set him in his
                                                                              14
place again. And when they arose early on the morrow morning, behold, Dagon
  14
was fallen upon his face to the ground before the ark of Yahweh; and the head of Dagon and both the palms of his hands were lying cut off upon the threshold; only the stump of Dagon was left to him. Therefore neither the priests of Dagon, nor any that come into Dagon's house, tread on the threshold of Dagon in Ashdod, unto this day, but they leap over it.
                            15
"But the hand of Yahweh was heavy upon them of Ashdod, and he destroyed them, and smote them with boils, even Ashdod and its borders. And when the men of Ashdod saw that it was so, they said, The ark of the God of Israel shall not abide with us, for his hand is sore upon us, and upon Dagon our god. They sent therefore and gathered all the lords of the Philistines unto them, and said,
                                          16
What shall we do with the ark of the God of Israel? And they answered, Let the ark of the God of Israel be carried about unto Gath. And they carried the ark
                                              17
of the God of Israel there. And it was so, that, after they had carried it about, the hand of Yahweh was against the city with a very great destruction; and he smote the men of the city, both small and great; and boils broke out upon them. They therefore sent the ark of God to Ekron. And it came to pass, as the ark of
                                  18
God came to Ekron, that the Ekronites cried out, saying, They have brought about the ark of the God of Israel to us, to slay us and our people. So they sent and gathered together all the lords of the Philistines, and they said, Send away

(Continued on Sheet 2)

the ark of the God of Israel, and let it go again to its own place, that it slay us
<u>19</u>

not, and our people. For there was a deadly destruction throughout all the city;
<u>19</u>

the hand of God was very heavy there. And the men that died not were smitten

with the boils and the cry of the city went up to heaven.

"And the ark of Yahweh was in the country of the Philistines seven months.

And the Philistines called for the priests and the diviners, saying, What shall we
<u>20</u>

do with the ark of Yahweh? show us wherewith we shall send it to its place.

And they said, If ye send away the ark of the God of Israel, send it not empty;

but be sure to return him a trespass-offering; then ye shall be healed, and it shall
<u>21</u>

be known to you why his hand is not removed from you. Then said they, What

shall be the trespass-offering which we shall return to him? And they said, Five
<u>22</u>

golden boils, and five golden mice, according to the number of the lords of the
<u>22</u>   <u>23</u>

Philistines; for one plague was on you all, and on your lords. Wherefore ye

shall make images of your boils, and images of your mice that mar the land; and
<u>23</u>

ye shall give glory unto the God of Israel; peradventure he will lighten his hand

from off you, and from off your gods, and from off your land."

24. The time-setting of the foregoing narrative is ....

....

25. The narrative is from the biblical book of ....

x. Number of items adequately interpreted = ... × 4 = Score.........

Number each item in the second column to correspond with that word in the first column with which it is correctly associated.

1. Abner   ( ) Benjaminite who cursed and stoned King David
2. Absalom   ( ) Benjaminite who headed a rebellion against King David
3. Achish
4. Adonijah   ( ) Captain of King David's bodyguard who supported Solo-
5. Adullam   mon for the kingship
6. Ammon   ( ) Cave where David once had to hide for safety
7. Amnon   ( ) Chief-of-staff of King David's army
8. Araunah   ( ) Chief priest appointed by King David
9. Bathsheba
10. Beersheba   ( ) David bought his threshing floor as a site for the temple
11. Benaiah   ( ) David's capital as king of Judah
12. Bichri   ( ) David's father
13. Cherethites
14. Elah   ( ) First woman David married
15. Geshur   ( ) King Saul's son and successor
16. Gezer   ( ) Led an unsuccessful coup to become king at time of David's
17. Goliath   death
18. Hebron
19. Ishbosheth ( ) Philistine bodyguard of King David
20. Ittai   ( ) Philistine with whom David was allied when an outlaw
21. Jebusites   ( ) Prophet who rebuked King David
22. Jeshimon
23. Jesse   ( ) Son of David who headed a rebellion against his father
24. Joab   ( ) Son of David who violated his half-sister, Tamar
25. Jonathan   ( ) Title of King David's prime minister
26. Michal   ( ) Valley where David killed Goliath
27. Michmash
28. Millo   ( ) Wife of Uriah the Hittite
29. Nathan
30. Nob
31. Pelethites
32. Ramah
33. Recorder
34. Scribe
35. Sheba
36. Shimei
37. Tamar
38. Uriah
39. Zadok
40. Zelek

xi §§2–5. Number of items correctly numbered = ... × 5 = Score........

Give the information necessary to complete the following account of

SOLOMON

Solomon was the son of King David and .... He became king after a contest with his older half-brother, ... In this contest Solomon had the backing of such prominent men as (1)........................., (2)........................... and (3).............................. His brother had been supported by (1)................ and (2)............................... After Solomon became king, he executed this brother because.............. ....

Source material for a history of the reign of King Solomon is in the biblical books of ....

Solomon inherited from his father a sizable empire which extended from .... to .... Two subject states at once successfully revolted, namely (1)................ under its king, ... and (2)........................ under its king, ...

Solomon's governmental organization included the following officials:
(1)............................ (2)................................
(3)............................ (4)................................
(5)............................ (6)................................
(7)............................ (8)................................
(9)............................

In international relations Solomon had significant contacts with
(1).. and
(2)..

Solomon built in Jerusalem an ensemble of state buildings, including
(1)............................ (2)................................
(3)............................ (4)................................
(5)............................ (6)................................
He also built Millo, which was .... At strategic points in his realm he constructed fortresses, for two purposes:
(1)..
(2)..

Commercial enterprises sponsored by Solomon were (1)................ .... and
(2)..

Solomon became heavily involved in debt to King Hiram of . . . .

for . . . .

Ultimately Solomon liquidated this debt by . . . .

. . . .

Some of the constructive accomplishments of Solomon's reign were

(1) . . . .

(2) . . . .

(3) . . . .

(4) . . . .

(5) . . . .

An unsuccessful conspiracy against Solomon was instigated by . . . .

. . . . in favor of . . . .

The latter had to flee to . . . . to escape Solomon's vengeance.

Solomon died, most probably, in the year . . . .

xi §§6–7. Number of items adequately stated = ... × 2 = Score. . . . .

68

Number each item in the second column to correspond with that word in the first column with which it is correctly associated.

1. Abi
2. Ahab
3. Ahijah
4. Canaan
5. Cuneiform
6. David
7. Decalogue
8. Ethan
9. Gad
10. Galileans
11. Gezer
12. Gideon
13. Gilead
14. Heman
15. Hieroglyphic
16. Jashar
17. Jesus
18. Joshua
19. I Kings
20. II Kings
21. Law
22. Moab
23. Moses
24. Nabal
25. Nathan
26. Old Semitic Script
27. Psalmody
28. Prophecy
29. Ras Shamra
30. Samaritans
31. Samuel
32. I Samuel
33. II Samuel
34. Scribes
35. Seer
36. Siloam
37. Solomon
38. Succoth
39. Wisdom
40. Ziba

( ) A "lost book" of poetry quoted in the Old Testament

( ) Bible book which contains "The Song of the Bow"

( ) Characteristic Egyptian writing

( ) Country where an inscription in Old Semitic Script was set up by King Mesha

( ) Earliest type of writing used by Hebrews

( ) First direct reference to writing among the Hebrews is about it

( ) He is said to have written a book "On the Nature of the Hebrew Kingdom"

( ) Hebrew farmer mentioned in the "Gezer Calendar"

( ) His name is connected with the first direct reference to writing among the Hebrews

( ) Instituted the practice of keeping royal records

( ) Literary type with which the name of King David is intimately associated

( ) Literary type with which the name of Moses is intimately associated

( ) Literary type with which the name of King Solomon is intimately associated

( ) Prophet of King David's time by or about whom a book was written

( ) Site in the Shephelah where important inscriptions in Old Semitic Script were found

( ) They now still employ the Old Semitic Script

( ) Universal medium of official correspondence in the fourteenth century B.C.

( ) Where a boy wrote out a list of the prominent men for Gideon

( ) Where an eighth-century inscription in Old Semitic Script was made, near Jerusalem

( ) Where clay tablets written with a cuneiform alphabet were found

xii §§1–2. Number of items correctly numbered = ... × 5 = Score.......

Indicate whether the following statements are true or false by underscoring the appropriate word. Correct any false statement on the blank line following it; the first half of any statement must be retained in any proposed correction.

1. In the tenth century B.C. Hebrew religion / became a state cult.   TRUE   FALSE   1
   ....

2. The Jerusalem temple was built on a site / purchased from Uriah the Hittite.   TRUE   FALSE   2
   ....

3. The Jerusalem temple was built by / King David.   TRUE   FALSE   3
   ....

4. The Jerusalem temple was constructed as a place for / the assembling of worshipers.   TRUE   FALSE   4
   ....

5. The Jerusalem temple faced / east.   TRUE   FALSE   5
   ....

6. The Great Altar of Burnt Offering was located / directly in front of the temple.   TRUE   FALSE   6
   ....

7. The Table of Showbread was in / the High Place of the Jerusalem temple.   TRUE   FALSE   7
   ....

8. The Most Holy Place was / that part of the Jerusalem temple into which one entered directly from the door.   TRUE   FALSE   8
   ....

9. The innermost sanctuary of the Jerusalem temple was called / the Holy Place.   TRUE   FALSE   9
   ....

10. The Holy Place of the temple contained / the lampstands.   TRUE   FALSE   10
    ....

11. The Most Holy Place of the temple contained / the Ark.   TRUE   FALSE   11
    ....

12. Teraphim were / the winged figures above the Ark.   TRUL   FALSE   12
    ....

13. The cherubim were located / in the court of the temple.   TRUE   FALSE   13
    ....

71

14. Jachin was / a sacred column in the Jerusalem temple court.   TRUE   FALSE   14

....

15. Boaz was / a bronze snake worshiped in the court of the Jerusalem temple.   TRUE   FALSE   15

....

16. The molten sea was / an alternative name for the Dead Sea.   TRUE   FALSE   16

....

17. A prophet rebuked King David for / his sin with Beer-sheba.   TRUE   FALSE   17

....

18. Zadok was / a priest appointed by King David.   TRUE   FALSE   18

....

19. Gad was / David's seer.   TRUE   FALSE   19

....

20. Beeliada was / a son of David.   TRUE   FALSE   20

....

21. Ahijah was / a prophet in the time of King Solomon.   TRUE   FALSE   21

....

22. Solomon built a shrine in Jerusalem for / Ashtoreth.   TRUE   FALSE   22

....

23. Rimmon was / a son of King Solomon.   TRUE   FALSE   23

....

24. Chemosh was / the god of Moab.   TRUE   FALSE   24

....

25. Soil from Samaria was carried to Damascus by / Nahum the Syrian, so that he might worship Yahweh.   TRUE   FALSE   25

....

===

xii §§3–4. Number of statements correctly judged and adequately corrected =
.... × 4 = Score........

The following either were or were not causes for the disruption of the Hebrew Dual Monarchy; indicate which by underscoring Yes or No.

1. (1) The Hebrews were subjected to heavy taxation and forced labor in order to carry on extensive building enterprises.   YES NO (1)

    (2) King Solomon worshiped the deities of his foreign wives and build shrines for those deities in Jerusalem.   YES NO (2)

    (3) A policy of imperialism was begun by King David and was extended by his successor.   YES NO (3)

    (4) Absalom stirred up a revolt in order that he might become king.   YES NO (4)

    (5) Solomon promoted commerce, both overland and by sea.   YES NO (5)

    (6) Solomon instituted a systematic tax collection scheme from which Judah was exempt.   YES NO (6)

    (7) A request of the people that their grievances be redressed was refused by the king.   YES NO (7)

    (8) The northern tribesmen were independent and progressive, and the southern tribesmen were reactionary.   YES NO (8)

    (9) Jeroboam of Ephraim was incited to rebellion by a prophet.   YES NO (9)

    (10) An age-long and deep-seated jealousy existed between the Joseph tribes and Judah.   YES NO (10)

    (11) Sheshonk the Egyptian pharaoh invaded Judah and Israel.   YES NO (11)

    (12) Rehoboam said, "My father made your yoke heavy, but I will add to your yoke; my father chastised you with whips, but I will chastise you with scorpions."   YES NO (12)

Give the information necessary to complete the following statements.

2. After the disruption of the Dual Monarchy, ... held the greater economic and geographical resources.

3. After the disruption, ... retained the dynasty of David.

4. After the disruption, ... retained control of the temple.

5. After the disruption, new royal sanctuaries were established at ....
....

6. There was once a fifty years' war between Judah and Israel. It began when .... was king of Judah and .... was king of Israel. The war was ended by King .... of Judah and King .... of Israel.
7. The "house of Jeroboam" was ....
8. Asa hired .... to invade Israel.
9. Baasha was ....
10. The formula, "There is no inheritance in the son of Jesse," meant ....
....
....

Interpret the following story by appropriate comment on each numbered item.

"And <u>Rehoboam</u> went to <u>Shechem</u>; for <u>all Israel</u> were come to Shechem to
     1   2   3
make him king. And it came to pass, when <u>Jeroboam</u> the son of Nebat heard
                               4
of it (who was yet in <u>Egypt, where he had fled</u> from the presence of king Solo-
                   5
mon, and Jeroboam was living in Egypt, and they sent for him), that Jeroboam
and all the assembly of Israel came, and said to Rehoboam, Thy father made
our yoke grievous; now therefore make thou <u>the grievous service of thy father,</u>
                                      6
<u>and his heavy yoke</u> which he put upon us, lighter, and we will serve thee. And
          6
he said unto them, Depart yet for three days, then come again to me. And the
people departed.

"And king Rehoboam consulted the <u>old men that stood before Solomon</u> his
                                     7
father while he yet lived, saying, What advice do ye give that I may answer this
people? And they spake unto him, saying, If thou wilt <u>be a servant unto this</u>
                                         8
<u>people</u> this day, and wilt serve them, and answer them, and speak good words
 8
to them, then they will be thy servants for ever. But he forsook the counsel of
the old men which they had given him, and consulted the young men that were
grown up with him, who stood before him. And he said unto them, What counsel give ye, that we may answer this people, who have spoken to me, saying, Make
the yoke which thy father did put upon us lighter? And <u>the young men that</u>
                                        9
<u>were grown up with him</u> spake unto him, saying, Thus shalt thou speak unto
          9
this people that spake unto thee, saying, Thy father made our yoke heavy, but
make thou it lighter unto us; thus shalt thou say unto them, My little finger is
thicker than my father's loins. And now whereas my father did lade you with
a heavy yoke, <u>I will add to your yoke</u>; my father chastised you with whips, but
               10
I will chastise you with <u>scorpions.</u>
                         11

"So Jeroboam and all the people came to Rehoboam the third day, as the

king had appointed, saying, Come to me again the third day. And the king answered the people roughly, and forsook the old men's counsel that they gave him, and spake to them after the counsel of the young men, saying, My father made your yoke heavy, and I will add to your yoke; my father also chastised you with whips, but I will chastise you with scorpions. So the king did not listen to the people; for it was a thing brought to pass by the LORD, that he might per-
<u>12</u>
form his word, which the LORD spake by Ahijah the Shilonite to Jeroboam the
                                     13   14
son of Nebat.

"When all Israel saw that the king hearkened not unto them, the people answered the king, saying, What portion have we in David? neither have we inheritance in the son of Jesse; to your tents, O Israel; now see to thine own
               15   16   17
house, David. So Israel departed unto their tents. But as for the children of
   17   18
Israel that lived in the cities of Judah, Rehoboam reigned over them. Then
 18
king Rehoboam sent Adoram, who was over the men in the labor gangs; and all
                                         19
Israel stoned him to death. Then king Rehoboam made speed to get him up to his chariot, to flee to Jerusalem. So Israel rebelled against the house of David unto this day. And it came to pass that, when all Israel heard that Jeroboam had returned, they sent and called him unto the congregation, and made him king over all Israel; there was none that followed the house of David, but the tribe of Judah only."

20. The foregoing narrative is from the biblical book of ....

Give the information necessary to complete the following statements.

The era of the two Hebrew kingdoms of .... and ....
began with their separation after the [event] ....
....,
which occurred in .... B.C. The study of this era is simplified by bearing
in mind the climactic events toward which the history moves. These are
(1)..,
which occurred in .... B.C.; and (2)................................
................................, which occurred in .... B.C.
Of all the causes leading up to these climactic events, the most important was
.... in nature, and there were two phases to it, external
and internal. The external factor was ....
....
The internal factor was .... and
....

The principal source material for a history of this era is found in the biblical
books of ....
The author of that narrative did not write history for history's sake, but history
for the sake of religion. That is, he selected for narration such incidents from
the careers of the two nations as would illustrate his theory that material well-
being and permanence depended exclusively upon ....
....
and upon ....,
and that national ruin followed inevitably upon ....
.... and upon ....
....
The author uniformly condemns all rulers of one of the kingdoms because .....
....
....
Additional light upon the era of the two kingdoms is shed by certain biblical writ-
ings of the highest possible historical value, namely, ...
....
Secondary material about this era is in the biblical book of ....

The biblical material can be supplemented by data from archaeological monu-

ments, which often reveal facts about which the Bible is silent. An example is
the ....
which discloses that ....
....
....

Interpret the following story by appropriate comment on each numbered item.

"Naboth the Jezreelite had a vineyard, which was in Jezreel, hard by the
$\underset{1}{}$
palace of Ahab king of Samaria. And Ahab spake unto Naboth, saying, Give me
$\underset{2}{}$ $\underset{3}{}$
thy vineyard, that I may have it for a garden of herbs, because it is near unto my
house; and I will give thee for it a better vineyard than it; or, if it seem good to
thee, I will give thee the worth of it in money. And Naboth said to Ahab,
The LORD forbid it me, that I should give the inheritance of my fathers unto
$\underset{4}{}$
thee. And Ahab came into his house heavy and displeased because of the word
which Naboth the Jezreelite had spoken to him; for he had said, I will not give
thee the inheritance of my fathers. And he laid him down upon his bed, and
turned away his face, and would eat no bread.

"But Jezebel his wife came to him, and said unto him, Why is thy spirit so
$\underset{5}{}$
sad, that thou eatest no bread? And he said unto her, Because I spake unto
Naboth the Jezreelite, and said unto him, Give me thy vineyard for money;
or else, if it please thee, I will give thee another vineyard for it; and he answered,
I will not give thee my vineyard. And Jezebel his wife said unto him, Dost thou
$\underset{6}{}$
now govern the kingdom of Israel? arise, and eat bread, and let thy heart be
$\underset{6}{}$
merry; I will give thee the vineyard of Naboth the Jezreelite. So she wrote letters
$\underset{7}{}$
in Ahab's name, and sealed them with his seal, and sent the letters unto the elders
$\underset{8}{}$ $\underset{9}{}$
and to the nobles that were in his city, and dwelling with Naboth. And she
wrote in the letters, saying, Proclaim a fast, and set Naboth on high among the
people; and set two debased fellows before him, to bear witness against him,
saying, Thou hast cursed God and the king. And then carry him out, and stone
$\underset{10}{}$ $\underset{11}{}$
him, that he may die.
$\underset{11}{}$

"And the men of his city, even the elders and the nobles who lived in his city,

did as Jezebel had sent unto them, according as it was written in the letters
which she had sent unto them. They proclaimed a fast, and set Naboth on high
among the people. And the two vile men came in and sat before him; and the
evil men bare witness against him, even against Naboth, in the presence of the
people, saying, Naboth cursed God and the king. Then they carried him forth
out of the city, and stoned him to death. Then they sent to Jezebel, saying,
Naboth is stoned, and is dead, And it came to pass, when Jezebel heard that
Naboth was stoned, and was dead, that Jezebel said to Ahab, Arise, take possession of the vineyard of Naboth the Jezreelite, which he refused to give thee
for money; for Naboth is not alive, but dead. And it came to pass, when Ahab
heard that Naboth was dead, that Ahab rose up to go down to the vineyard of
Naboth the Jezreelite, to take possession of it.

"And the word of the LORD came to Elijah the Tishbite, saying, Arise, go
down to meet Ahab king of Israel, who lives in Samaria; behold, he is in the
vineyard of Naboth, whither he is gone down to possess it. And thou shalt speak
unto him, saying, Thus saith the LORD, Hast thou killed, and also taken possession? And thou shalt speak unto him, saying, Thus saith the LORD, In the place
where dogs licked the blood of Naboth shall dogs lick thy blood, even thine. And
Ahab said to Elijah, Hast thou found me, O mine enemy? And he answered, I
have found thee, because thou hast sold thyself to work evil in the sight of the
LORD. Behold, I will bring evil upon thee, and will completely sweep thee away
and will cut off from Ahab every male child, and him that is shut up and him
that is left free in Israel, and will make thy house like the house of Jeroboam the
son of Nebat, and like the house of Baasha the son of Ahijah, for the provocation
wherewith thou hast provoked me to anger and made Israel to sin. And of Jezebel also spake the LORD, saying, The dogs shall eat Jezebel by the wall of Jezreel.

(*Continued on Sheet 2*)

Him that dieth of Ahab in the city the dogs shall eat; and him that dieth in the field shall the birds of the air eat. . . .

"And it came to pass, when Ahab heard those words, that he rent his clothes, and put sackcloth upon his flesh, and fasted, and lay in sackcloth, and went softly. And the word of the LORD came to Elijah the Tishbite, saying, Seest thou how Ahab humbleth himself before me? because he humbleth himself before
[20]
me, I will not bring the evil in his days; but in his son's day I will bring the evil
[20]
upon his house."

xiv §4. Number of items adequately interpreted = ... × 5 = Score. . . . . . .

Give the information necessary to complete the following statements.

1. The kingdom of Judah, throughout its history, was ruled by the dynasty of
.............., excepting for one interruption when ....
seized the throne following the death of .... After
six years this usurper ....
....

2. Hamath was ....

3. A military and commercial alliance between Israel and Phoenicia was formed
in the reign of King .... of Israel.

4. One of the noteworthy accomplishments of King Omri of Israel was the
founding of a capital city at ....

5. Political revolution, both in Israel and in Damascus, was plotted by the
Hebrew prophet .... His motive may have been ......
....
As a result of this revolution .... became king of Israel.

6. The Moabite Stone was set up by King .... of Moab. It
states that Moab became subject to Israel in the time of King ....
.... of Israel, and continued so for forty years. The Stone celebrates
the independence of Moab which was won about the year ....
when .... was king of Israel.

7. The long period of the subjugation of Israel to Damascus began in the time
of King .... of Israel and was caused by the fact that
he ....
.... This subjugation came to an end when
....

8. The Black Obelisk of the Assyrian king .... portrays
the Israelite king .... as ....
....

xiv §§2–5. Number of items adequately stated = ... × 5 = Score........

Indicate whether the following statements are true or false by underscoring the appropriate word. Correct any false statement on the blank line following it; the first half of any statement must be retained in any proposed correction.

1. The only ruler of Judah who was not of the Davidic line was / Athaliah.   TRUE   FALSE   1

....

2. Amos was / a prophet of the time of King Jeroboam I of Israel.   TRUE   FALSE   2

....

3. King Omri of Israel changed the capital city / from Tirzah to Samaria.   TRUE   FALSE   3

....

4. The "House of Omri" was / King Omri's palace in Samaria.   TRUE   FALSE   4

....

5. King Omri of Israel formed an alliance with / Phoenicia.   TRUE   FALSE   5

....

6. Ethbaal [Ithobaal] was / priest of Ashtart in Phoenicia.   TRUE   FALSE   6

....

7. Mesha was / a king of Moab.   TRUE   FALSE   7

....

8. Ahab of Israel and Benhadad of Damascus were / allies in the battle of Karkar in 854 B.C.   TRUE   FALSE   8

....

9. Hamath was / a general in the Syrian army.   TRUE   FALSE   9

....

10. Ramoth-gilead was / a city in Eastjordania.   TRUE   FALSE   10

....

11. Micaiah-ben-Imlah was / a Syrian general opposed to making war on Israel.   TRUE   FALSE   11

....

12. Elijah was / priest in Samaria during the reign of King Ahab.   TRUE   FALSE   12

....

13. Elijah was / the successor of Elisha.   TRUE   FALSE   13

....

85

14. Elisha incited / a general in the army to stir up a revolution against the ruling dynasty in Israel. TRUE FALSE 14

....

15. Naboth was / one of the kings of Israel. TRUE FALSE 15

....

16. Jehu was / the last king of the dynasty of Omri. TRUE FALSE 16

17. Shalmaneser III was king of Assyria / during Jehu's reign. TRUE FALSE 17

....

18. Jehu was / allied with Damascus against Shalmaneser of Assyria in 842 B.C. TRUE FALSE 18

....

19. The Black Obelisk of Shalmaneser pictures / the tribute paid to him by the king of Judah. TRUE FALSE 19

....

20. King J(eh)oash of Judah / compelled Hazael of Damascus to pay tribute. TRUE FALSE 20

....

21. Jezebel was / the wife of King Ahaz. TRUE FALSE 21

....

22. King Amaziah of Judah / initiated a war against Israel. TRUE FALSE 22

....

23. The first half of the eighth century B.C. was / a period of continual warfare between both Hebrew kingdoms. TRUE FALSE 23

....

24. King Azariah of Judah was / an ally of Uzziah. TRUE FALSE 24

....

25. The reign of King Jeroboam II over Israel was / a period of great prosperity. TRUE FALSE 25

....

xiv. Number of statements correctly judged and adequately corrected = ...

$\times$ 4 = Score.........

Give the information necessary to complete the following statements.

Assyria experienced a rebirth of power in the year .... B.C., with the accession of the mighty monarch ....
In the year 734 B.C. King .... of Damascus and King .... of Israel attempted to form a coalition of Syrian states against this new Assyrian monarch. They invaded Judah and besieged Jerusalem in order to compel King .... of Judah to join the coalition. The Judahite king was thoroughly frightened by this threat, for he had only recently suffered military reverses in the south, where the ....
.... had taken ....
away from Judah, and also in the west, where the ....
had taken .... away from Judah.

The prophet .... advised the Judahite king to keep out of the Syrian coalition. The prophet characterized the kings of Damascus and Israel as ....
The policy which this prophet advocated had two aspects, (1).............
.... and
(2)..
What the Judahite king actually did, however, was ....
.... The immediate result of this action for Judah was ....
.... Its ultimate outcome for Judah was
....
....

The Syrian coalition proved disastrous for its principals. Israel lost (1).......................... and (2)..........................
The kingdom of Damascus was obliterated in the year .... Captives from Damascus and from the conquered portions of Israel were deported to
....
In thus disposing of the exiles the Assyrian conqueror's intention was ....
....
....

The ensuing ten years was a time of political anarchy and intrigue in Israel. Eventually open rebellion led to the invasion of Israel and the siege of its capital city .... The city fell in the year ....
Israelite captives were carried off into exile by ....
.... These exiles are known historically as ....
....

xv §§1–3. Number of items adequately stated = ... × 4 = Score........

Check the country with which each of the following is correctly associated.

	Ara-bia	As-syria	Baby-lonia	Egypt	Is-rael	Ju-dah	Phi-listia	Phoe-nicia	Syria
1. Amon									
2. Arpad									
3. Ashdod									
4. Ashurbanipal									
5. Azariah									
6. Bit Yakin									
7. Esarhaddon									
8. Gaza									
9. Hanno									
10. Iati'e									
11. Josiah									
12. Khorsabad									
13. Manasseh									
14. Merodach-baladan									
15. Micah									
16. Padi									
17. Psamtik									
18. Raphia									
19. Samsi									
20. Sargon									
21. Sennacherib									
22. Shabaka									
23. Tyre									
24. Uzziah									
25. Zephaniah									

xv §§4–5. Number of items correctly checked = ... × 4 = Score........

Indicate whether the following statements are true or false by underscoring the appropriate word. Correct any false statement on the blank line following it; the first half of any statement must be retained in any proposed correction.

1. Nineveh was / the greatest of all Assyrian sovereigns.   TRUE   FALSE   1

....

2. The Scythians / sacked Jerusalem in 626 B.C.   TRUE   FALSE   2

....

3. The Assyrian empire was conquered by / an alliance of the Medes with the Egyptians.   TRUE   FALSE   3

....

4. The Assyrian empire was supplanted by / the Chaldean empire.   TRUE   FALSE   4

....

5. The Chaldean empire was / supplanted by the Neo-Babylonian [=New Babylonian] empire.   TRUE   FALSE   5

....

6. The founder of the Neo-Babylonian empire was / Nebuchadrezzar.   TRUE   FALSE   6

....

7. During the period of Assyrian decline, the kingdom of Judah was / under Egyptian overlordship.   TRUE   FALSE   7

....

8. In 621 B.C. / a great persecution of prophets was started.   TRUE   FALSE   8

....

9. King Josiah lost his life / in battle with the Scythians.   TRUE   FALSE   9

....

10. The capital of the Assyrian empire was conquered in 612 B.C. by / the Egyptians.   TRUE   FALSE   10

....

11. The Assyrian empire came to an end with / the capture of its capital city in 612 B.C.   TRUE   FALSE   11

....

12. Necho was / the last king of Assyria, who escaped to Egypt after the fall of the empire's capital.   TRUE   FALSE   12

....

13. The Egyptians / defeated Nebuchadrezzar at the battle of Carchemish, 605 B.C.   TRUE   FALSE   13

....

14. When Nebuchadrezzar became overlord of Judah, / Jehoiakim was king of Judah.   TRUE   FALSE   14
....

15. Jehoiakim's revolt against Chaldea was prompted by / his belief that he had a superior army.   TRUE   FALSE   15
....

16. King Jehoiakim was / hostile to Jeremiah.   TRUE   FALSE   16
....

17. Jerusalem was besieged and captured in 597 B.C. by / Nebuchadrezzar.   TRUE   FALSE   17
....

18. Jeremiah advised the king to / surrender Samaria to prevent the destruction of its temple.   TRUE   FALSE   18
....

19. After the capture of Jerusalem in 597 B.C. / the population was left undisturbed because of payment of an indemnity.   TRUE   FALSE   19
....

20. Nebuchadrezzar deposed / King Jehoiakim of Judah and made Zedekiah king.   TRUE   FALSE   20
....

21. In 597 B.C. / King Jehoiakim was taken into captivity.   TRUE   FALSE   21
....

22. Judah's last king revolted against Nebuchadrezzar, / relying on Egypt for aid.   TRUE   FALSE   22
....

23. In July 586 B.C. Jerusalem was / captured and sacked by Nebuchadrezzar.   TRUE   FALSE   23
....

24. The first captivity of Judah occurred in / 586 B.C.   TRUE   FALSE   24
....

25. After 586 B.C. the Jews were / scattered in three countries, Babylonia, Judea, and Greece.   TRUE   FALSE   25
....

xvi. Number of statements correctly judged and adequately corrected = ...
$\times$ 4 = Score........

Give the information necessary to complete the following statements.

1. The basic occupations of the Hebrews throughout the period of the kingship were ....

2. "Hewers of stone" were ....

3. In Palestine, there were .... mines in .... and .... mines in ....

4. The "fuller's field" was located [where?] ....; it was so called because ....

5. The first important stimulus to trade was injected into Hebrew life by King .... His commercial enterprises included (1).. (2)..

6. A "sabbath day's journey" was a distance of about .... It was so called because ....

7. Trade and commerce necessitated measures, weights, and money. Originally parts of the human body were used as units of measurement; for example (1) the ...., which equalled ....; (2) the ...., which equalled ....; (3) the ...., which equalled .... Distance was measured in terms of the .... and the .... Area was measured in terms of the amount of .... or in terms of the amount of .... The unit of capacity was the ...., which equals about .... peck(s). Weight was indicated in terms of ...., each equal to about .... ounce(s), and in terms of ...., each equal to about .... pound(s). Money was by weight and in denominations of (1)............... (2)............... (3)............... The smallest of these was worth, if silver, about ....; if gold, about ....

8. The "king's weight" was ....

9. Some of the crafts and occupations which developed prior to 586 B.C. were (1)............................ (2)............................ (3)............................ (4)............................ (5)............................

10. A new day began at .... They told the time of day by
    such characteristic expressions as
    (1)...
    (2)...
    (3)...
    and the time of night was designated by ....
    A month extended from .... to ....
    A new year in the Jewish religious calendar begins on the ....
    day of the .... month, the name of which month is ......
    ....

xvii §§1–2. Number of items adequately stated = ... × 2 = Score........

94

Indicate whether the following statements are true or false by underscoring the appropriate word. Correct any false statement on the blank line following it; the first half of any statement must be retained in any proposed correction.

1. From earliest times Hebrew social thinking was / basically individualistic.

   .... TRUE FALSE 1

2. In the patriarchal age the political unit was / the family.

   .... TRUE FALSE 2

3. In a Hebrew community, social control was in the hands of / the elders.

   .... TRUE FALSE 3

4. The so-called Hebrew "judges" were / local military leaders.

   .... TRUE FALSE 4

5. The Hebrew aristocracy developed in the period of / the "judges."

   .... TRUE FALSE 5

6. The Hebrew aristocracy included / priests.

   .... TRUE FALSE 6

7. Native born Hebrews were made slaves of other Hebrews / for debt only.

   .... TRUE FALSE 7

8. The Book of the Covenant is / a law code found in Exodus.

   .... TRUE FALSE 8

9. The Deuteronomic Code ["D"] originated / in the sixth century B.C.

   .... TRUE FALSE 9

10. The "House of the Daughter of Pharaoh" was / the home in which Moses was reared in Egypt.

    .... TRUE FALSE 10

11. Millo was / the designer of a fortress tower built in the Jerusalem city wall.

    .... TRUE FALSE 11

12. The Jerusalem temple was / the most striking example of the Hebrew native style of architecture.

    .... TRUE FALSE 12

13. King Solomon's palace in Jerusalem was designed by / Philistine architects.   TRUE   FALSE   13

....

14. In the construction of the great buildings in Jerusalem in the time of King Solomon, the heavy manual labor was performed by / foreigners imported from Phoenicia.   TRUE   FALSE   14

....

15. The "House of the Forest of Lebanon" was / King Solomon's summer home in Syria.   TRUE   FALSE   15

....

16. In the planning of buildings and walls of Hebrew communities, the dominant idea was / facility of defense.   TRUE   FALSE   16

....

17. The two golden calves at the shrines in northern Israel were examples of / metal castings.   TRUE   FALSE   17

....

18. The two cherubim in the Jerusalem temple were / metal castings.   TRUE   FALSE   18

....

19. Figurines of the goddess Ashtart were / carved wooden images.   TRUE   FALSE   19

....

20. Hebrew pottery products followed the motifs of / Canaanite potters.   TRUE   FALSE   20

....

21. In the sphere of textile arts, the Hebrews showed most skill in / dyeing.   TRUE   FALSE   21

....

22. Hebrew music emphasized / rhythm.   TRUE   FALSE   22

....

23. Hebrew singing emphasized / the solo.   TRUE   FALSE   23

....

24. The psaltery was / a book of songs.   TRUE   FALSE   24

....

25. Dancing, among the Hebrews, was / usually in connection with religious ceremonies.   TRUE   FALSE   25

....

xvii §§3–4. Number of statements correctly judged and adequately corrected =
.... × 4 = Score........

Indicate whether the following statements are true or false by underscoring the appropriate word. Correct any false statement on the blank line following it; the first half of any statement must be retained in any proposed correction.

1. Hebrew literature was / patterned after Canaanite literary models. TRUE FALSE 1

   ....

2. The "Book of the Chronicles of the Kings of Judah," which is frequently referred to in First Kings, means / the Bible book now known as "First Chronicles." TRUE FALSE 2

   ....

3. The "Book of the Chronicles of the Kings of Israel" is / the same as the Bible book of "Second Chronicles." TRUE FALSE 3

   ....

4. In the seventh century B.C. Hebrew literary activity was / stimulated by Assyrian culture. TRUE FALSE 4

   ....

5. The so-called "Lost Books" of the Hebrews are / the books now known as the Apocrypha. TRUE FALSE 5

   ....

6. The first attempt at writing a connected history of Hebrew origins was / in the ninth century B.C. TRUE FALSE 6

   ....

7. The conception of God in the early Judean narratives ["J"] is / anthropomorphic. TRUE FALSE 7

   ....

8. The Ephraimite prophetic history ["E"] is / a compilation of early Hebrew traditions made by writers in the northern kingdom of Israel. TRUE FALSE 8

   ....

9. "J" was written / before "E". TRUE FALSE 9

   ....

10. The Ephraimite prophetic history ["E"] emphasizes / dominant personalities, especially the prophets. TRUE FALSE 10

    ....

11. The early Judean ["J"] and the Ephraimite ["E"] prophetic narratives were combined into "JE" / most likely before the downfall of the kingdom of Israel. TRUE FALSE 11

    ....

12. The first Old Testament book written was / Genesis. TRUE FALSE 12

    ....

97

13. The first complete Bible books written in the eighth century B.C. were / Amos and Hosea.　　TRUE　FALSE　13

....

14. The oldest one of the Old Testament books (as they now are) is mainly / poetry.　　TRUE　FALSE　14

....

15. Meter in Hebrew poetry means / the rhythmic arrangement of long and short syllables.　　TRUE　FALSE　15

....

16. The *kinah* was / a Hebrew measure of area.　　TRUE　FALSE　16

....

17. Baruch was / a seventh-century prophet.　　TRUE　FALSE　17

....

18. The religious reformation in the time of King Josiah was stimulated by / the discovery of the "J" literature in the temple.　　TRUE　FALSE　18

....

19. The Deuteronomic Code ["D"] is characterized by / humanitarian interest.　　TRUE　FALSE　19

....

20. The Deuteronomic Code ["D"] dates / from the latter half of the seventh century B.C.　　TRUE　FALSE　20

....

21. The first of the writing prophets was / Elijah.　　TRUE　FALSE　21

....

22. The Genesis story of Abraham's attempt to offer Isaac as a burnt sacrifice is an example of / "E's" narrative art.　　TRUE　FALSE　22

....

23. The Genesis story of the doom of Sodom is an example of / "J's" narrative art.　　TRUE　FALSE　23

....

24. The word book, as used in the Old Testament, means / a codex, that is, a stack of animal-skin pages fastened together.　　TRUE　FALSE　24

....

25. The earliest part of the Bible to be regarded as sacred literature (holy scripture) was / Genesis.　　TRUE　FALSE　25

....

xvii § 5. Number of statements correctly judged and adequately corrected =
.... × 4 = Score........

Number each item in the second column to correspond with that word in the first column with which it is correctly associated.

1. Aaron	( ) A sacred wooden post, possibly capped by some
2. Ahaz	carved image
3. Amos	( ) An upright sacred column in the Jerusalem temple
4. Anthropomorphism	court
5. Apostasy	
6. Ark	( ) Ancient Palestinian local community sanctuary
7. Asa	( ) Conception of God as having a bodily form like
8. Asherah	man
9. Ashtart	
10. Bethel	( ) Desertion of one's religion for some new religion
11. Boaz	( ) Historical narratives which originated in the eighth
12. Bronze bulls	century B.C.
13. Bronze serpent	
14. Carmel	( ) Household gods
15. Cherubim	( ) King who built the Jerusalem temple
16. Dan	( ) King who established the national shrines of north-
17. "E"	ern Israel
18. Gilgal	
19. Golden calves	( ) Monthly holy day
20. Hezekiah	( ) Most important sanctuary in northern Israel
21. High place	( ) Most noted religious images in northern Israel
22. Hosea	
23. Isaiah	( ) Mother-goddess
24. "J"	( ) Mountain associated with the prophet Elijah
25. Jachin	( ) Object of cult worship made by Moses
26. Jehoash	( ) Prophetic narratives which originated in the ninth
27. Jehu	century B.C.
28. Jeroboam	
29. Josiah	( ) Representing the deity as having an animal form
30. Manasseh	( ) Supports on which the bronze laver in the Jeru-
31. Micah	salem temple court rested
32. Most Holy Place	
33. New Moon Day	( ) Weekly holy day
34. Rechabite	( ) Winged figures in the interior of the Jerusalem
35. Sabbath	temple.
36. Sinai	
37. Solomon	
38. Teraphim	
39. Theriomorphism	
40. Yahwism	

xviii §§1–2. Number of items correctly numbered = ... × 5 = Score.......

Give the information necessary to complete the following account of

AMOS

The prophet Amos lived in the .... century B.C. He was a native

of .... in the land of .... on the edge
      2   3

of the area known as ....
                             4

By occupation he was a ....
                      5

At the time of Amos's prophetic activity, the ruler of the Kingdom of Israel

was .... and the ruler of Judah was ....
            6   7

.... It was an era of ....
   7   8

The social-ethical problem which such an era presented was ....
                                  9

....
                            9

Amos said, "I am no prophet, neither am I a prophet's son," by which he

meant ....
                        10

....
                        10

In Amos's time, conventional prophesying consisted in ....
                              11

.... rather than in spoken wisdom.
                    11

The emergence of Amos marks a new development in Hebrew prophecy. He is

known as the first of the .... prophets, because
                          12

....
                        13

On a certain festival day at the sanctuary of ....
                          14

in ...., Amos blazed forth in an impassioned speech. Just
            15

why Amos was at that shrine we can only conjecture; probably it was because

....
                        16

....
                        16

At any rate, the chief priest of the place, whose name was ....
                          17

sent word to the king, accusing Amos of ....
                        18

and at the same time ordered Amos out of the land.

Just what Amos said on that occasion is not specifically reported, but he may well have expressed such ideas as the following, which we find in his book:

"Thus saith the LORD: For three transgressions of Israel, and for four, I will not turn away the punishment thereof; because they have sold .... for .... and the ....
for a .... Ye who turn ....
to wormwood, and cast down .... to the ground, I know your manifold transgressions, and your mighty sins; ye who afflict the ...., who take a ...., and turn aside the .... from their right. Seek .... and not .... that ye may ....; and so the LORD, the God of hosts, will ...., as ye say. Hate the .... and love .... and establish .... in the .... Perhaps the LORD, the God of hosts, will be gracious unto the .... Woe unto you that desire the .... Why would you have the ....? It is darkness, and not light, even very dark, and no brightness in it. I hate, I despise your .... and I will not delight in .... Though ye offer me .... and .... I will not accept them; neither will I regard the .... of your .... Take thou away from me the noise of thy ...., for I will not hear .... But let .... as .... and .... as a ...."

That last sentence is the keynote, or golden gem, of the whole book of Amos.

(*Continued on Sheet 2*)

It shows why he is called the prophet of ....
49
Driven by the chief priest from the shrine, Amos went home. It was after that that he did the greatest thing of his life, namely ....'.........

....
50
....

xviii §3a.   Number of items adequately stated = ... × 2 = Score........

Give the information necessary to complete the following account of

HOSEA

The prophet Hosea lived in the .... century B.C. He did his prophetic
₁
work in the Kingdom of ...., of which he apparently
₂
was a native. His name, Hosea, means ....
₃

In Hosea's time his country had been enjoying at least a generation of
.... under King .... This fact was pop-
₄   ₅
ularly given a religious interpretation, namely, ...
₆
....

Hosea did not share this popular view because ....
₇
....

He was a married man. His wife's name was .... They
₈
had three children, a boy named ...., a girl named
₉
...................., and another boy named ....
₁₀   ₁₁
His wife proved faithless to him and left him, to live with other lovers, but
ultimately Hosea bought her back. This domestic tragedy gave its tone to his
prophetic preaching.

Hosea was a preacher of social righteousness. He denounced the moral cor-
ruption of his time, and said: "Hear the word of the LORD: My people are
destroyed for lack of ....; because thou hast rejected
₁₂
......................, I will also reject thee, that thou shalt be no priest
₁₂
to me; seeing thou hast forgotten ....;
₁₃
I will also forget thy children."

He denounced the revelry and debauchery connected with the feasts at the
religious shrines, and said: "I desire .... and not
₁₄
...................., and the ....
₁₅   ₁₆
more than ...." The moral attribute of God
₁₇

which this verse emphasizes is expressed also in his great saying: "The LORD is the God of hosts, the LORD is his name. Therefore turn thou to thy God; keep .... and ...., and wait on thy God continually."

18   19

Hosea proclaimed that national suffering would result from wrongdoing. This was not because of God's anger; "I will not execute the fierceness of mine anger, I will not return to destroy Ephraim; for I am ...., the .... in the midst of thee; and I will not come in anger." By their suffering God would steer them from worse disaster: "Come and let us return unto the LORD; for he hath .... and he will .... us; he hath .... and he will ...."

The fact that Hosea loved his wife with a love that would not let her go, but sought her and bought her back, inspired his exalted conception of God: "I will betroth thee unto me for ever; yea, I will betroth thee unto me in ...., and in ...., and in ...., and in .... I will even be-troth thee unto me in ....; and thou shalt know the LORD."

Hosea portrayed the attitude of God to Israel in terms of family relation-ships. For one thing, God is a .... to Israel: "And it shall be at that day, saith the LORD, that thou shalt call me .... (.......................), and shalt call me no more Baali (My master)." Again, God is a .... to Israel: "When Israel was a ...., then I .... him, and called........ .... out of Egypt. I taught Ephraim to ....; taking them on ...., but they knew not that I ...."

Hosea exhorted the people to repentance: "O Israel, return unto the LORD

(*Continued on Sheet 2*)

thy God." He expressed the assurance that "I will heal their backsliding, I will ....; for mine anger

40

is turned away from him."

===

xviii §3b.   Number of items adequately stated = ... × 2½ = Score.......

Give the information necessary to complete the following account of

ISAIAH

The prophet Isaiah was a native of the city of ....
.... He was a married man, but the name of his wife is not given. He had two sons,
to whom he gave symbolic names: they were ....,

2

which means ....,

3

and ...., which means

4

....

5

The prophetic career of Isaiah covered a period of approximately ....
years. He became a prophet "in the year that .... died."

6

7

His prophetic career spanned four crucial events in the history of the Hebrews:

(1)............ B.C., when ....;

8   9

(2)..........., when ....;

10   11

(3)..........., when ....; and

12   13

(4)..........., when ....

14   15

Isaiah was a statesman. Twice his advice was sought by Judean kings. The
first time was when King .... sought his counsel when

16

.... and ....

17   18

threatened to make war upon Judah because ....
....

19

Isaiah's advice to the king was ....

20

....

What the king actually did was ....

21

....

Some thirty-three years later King .... of Judah sought

22

Isaiah's advice in the crisis when ....

23

invaded Judah and besieged Jerusalem. There was much clamor that Judah

should resist this invasion by an alliance with ....,
^{24}
Isaiah's advice to the king was ....
^{25}
....

Later generations erroneously attributed to Isaiah the doctrine that Jerusalem
was ....; this came about because Isaiah in this time
^{26}
of crisis had said ....
^{27}
....
^{27}

When Isaiah began his prophetic career, the official religion in Judah was
.... This had come about under the
^{28}
sponsorship of .... The popular conception of
^{29}
religion rated .... as most important. But Isaiah rated
^{30}
.... as most important. There is strong emphasis upon so-
^{31}
cial ethics in the preaching of Isaiah. "Woe unto them that decree unright-
eous decrees, and to them that write iniquity; to turn aside ....
^{32}
.... from ....,
^{32} ^{33}
and to rob .... of ....,
^{34} ^{35}
that .... may be their prey, and that they may
^{36}
.... Other specific social iniqui-
^{37}
ties which he denounced were (1).......................................;
^{38}
(2)...;
^{39}
(3)...; and
^{40}
(4)...
^{41}
Such vices caused him to say, "I dwell in the midst of a people of ....
^{42}
.................................." "Woe unto them that call.........
^{43}
...................., and ...., that put
^{44} ^{44} ^{43}
.... for ...., and ....
^{45} ^{46} ^{46}
for ....; that put .... for ....,
^{45} ^{47} ^{48}
and .... for ...."
^{48} ^{47}
In such a social situation Isaiah appealed to his fellow countrymen: "Wash

(*Continued on Sheet 2*)

you, make you clean; put away . . . . from
                                              49

before mine eyes; cease to . . . . ; learn to . . . .
                                              50   51

. . . . ; seek . . . . ; relieve the . . . . ;
                              52   53

judge . . . . , plead for . . . .
                          54   55

Come now, and let us . . . . , saith
                                                      56

the LORD; though your sins . . . . , they shall
                                              57

. . . . ; though they . . . .
                      58   59
                                                                                                  ,,

. . . . , they shall be as . . . ."
                                                          60

"The LORD of hosts shall be exalted in . . . ., and God
                                                            61

the . . . . shall be sanctified in . . . ."
            62   63

Isaiah's creative contribution to the idea of God was the concept of . . . .

. . . . The best known verse expressing this is
                          64

" . . . ."
                                              65

Isaiah also conceived of God as the exalted ruler of nations, and his control even

reached to Judah's worst enemy, ..., whom
                                                      66

the prophet called the . . . . of the LORD'S . . . .
                              67   68

to visit punishment upon his sinful people.

Isaiah maintained that the integrity of his nation was guaranteed by loyalty

to God. "Thus saith the Lord GOD, the Holy One of Israel, In . . . .

. . . . and . . . . shall ye be saved; in
            69   70

. . . . and in . . . . shall be your strength."
            71   72

This principle was basic to his nation's welfare: "Thus saith the Lord GOD,

Behold I lay in Zion for a foundation a stone, a tried stone, a precious corner-

stone, a sure foundation: he that . . . .
                                                                                                          73
                                                                                                          ,,

. . . .

Upon that sure foundation rested Isaiah's hope for the future. In his doc-

trine of the future Isaiah emphasized two doctrines which had previously been

enunciated by the prophet Amos. One was the . . . .
                                                                        74

111

"There shall be a . . . . , upon all that is proud and
                                      74
lofty, and upon all that is lifted up, and it shall be . . . .
                                                                                            75
. . . ." The other doctrine was that of . . . .
                                                                                    76
. . . ., the importance of which in Isaiah's thinking is

attested by . . . .
                                                    77
Isaiah's hope for the future came to expression in one of the best known pas-

sages in the book of Isaiah, the prophecy of a warless world. "And it shall come

to pass in the last days, that the mountain of the LORD's house shall be . . . . . .

. . . . in the top of the mountains and shall be . . . .
            78   79
. . . . above the hills; and . . . .
                                                                                      80
shall . . . . And many . . . .
                          81   82
shall go and say, Come ye, let us . . . .
                                                                    83
mountain of the LORD, to . . . . the God of Jacob;
                                                    84
and he will . . . ., and we
                                            85
will . . . .; for out of Zion shall
                                  86
. . . . and the . . . .
                    87   88
. . . . from Jerusalem. And he will . . . .
                                                                                                89
. . . ., and will . . . .
                                                                            90
concerning . . . .; and they shall . . . .
                                      91   92
. . . . and

. . . .; nation
                                  93
. . . .,
                                        94
neither shall they learn war any more."

This idealistic future of peace was to come about as a by-product of some-

thing else: "Then . . . . shall dwell in the
                                        95
wilderness, and . . . . in the fruitful
                                  96
field. And the work of . . . . shall be peace,
                                                    96

(*Continued on Sheet 3*)

112

and the effect of .... [shall be] ....
96   97

and .... for ever."
98

Of the ultimate fate of Isaiah we cannot be certain, but there is a tradi-

tion that ....
99

in the time of King ....
100

xviii §3c. Number of items adequately stated = Score.......

Give the information necessary to complete the following account of

MICAH

The prophet Micah lived in the .... century B.C. He was a native

of ...., which was in that part of Palestine
2

known as .... His book manifests great
3

sympathy for ...., from which we may assume that
4

Micah himself was, by occupation, a ....
5

The opening verse of his book seems to indicate that his prophetic career

covered a total of .... years, but the only definite historical situation
6

with which his prophecy can be related was ....
7

.... in .... B.C.
8

That crisis brought special suffering to the ....
9

.... because ....
10

....

The full extent of that suffering may be grasped from the statement on the

archaeological monument known as ....
11

that ....
12

At that time the social status of the people of the area where Micah lived was

that of .... This had come about through
13

....
14

Micah placed the responsibility for this condition upon ....
15

.... who were living (as they thought) in

safety in .... The reason they thought they
16

were truly safe there was ....
17

....

This false belief arose from a misinterpretation of the preaching of the con-

temporary prophet .... Micah denounced such people
18

115

saying: "Because of *you*, Zion shall be . . . . ,
19
Jerusalem shall become . . . .
20
and the . . . .
21
as the . . . . "
22
    Micah set forth the doctrine that true religion consists in . . . .
23
. . . . rather than in . . . .
24
in a vigorous statement: "Wherewith shall I come . . . .
25
. . . . , and . . . . ?
26
. . . .
shall I come . . . .
27
. . . . ? Will the LORD . . . .
. . . .
28 29
. . . . ?
shall I give . . . .
30 31
. . . . ?
He hath shewed . . . . ;
32
and what doth the LORD . . . .
33
but . . . .
34–36
. . . . ?"

    Micah's preaching prompted King . . . . to institute a
37
religious reform. This fact and Micah's famous utterance (items 19–22 above)
saved the life, in a later century, of the prophet . . . .
38
whose contemporaries wanted to kill him for saying the same thing.

    Micah may have lived on into the reign of King . . . .
39
What his ultimate fate was is wholly unknown. But a later generation erected
an enduring monument to his career, namely . . . .
40

---

xviii §3d.   Number of items adequately stated = ... × 2½ = Score . . . .

Give the information necessary to complete the following statements.

1. Apostasy means ....
....

2. Kings of Judah whose reigns were periods of apostasy were
   (1) King .... in the .... century
   (2) King .... in the .... century
   (3) King .... in the .... century
   (4) King .... in the .... century

3. Specific features of such apostasy were
   (1).., an example
       of which was ....
   (2).., an example
       of which was ....
   (3)..
   (4)..
   (5)..

4. Noteworthy religious reformations occurred in the reigns of
   (1) King .... in the .... century
       Specific features of this reformation were
       (a)..
       (b)..
       (c)..
   (2) King .... in the year ....
       Specific features of this reformation were
       (a)..
       (b)..
       (c)..
       (d)..
       (e)..
       The defect in this reformation was twofold:
       (a)..
       (b)..

5. "D" was ....

6. "D" affirms the principle of .... as the basic motiva-
   tion of social life. Specific applications of this principle by "D" were:
   (1)..
   ....
   (2)..
   ....

(3)..
....
(4)..
....
(5)..
....

7. The ultimate disposition made of "D" was ....
.... This was done when
....

8. Asherah was ....
....

9. Ashtoreth was ....
....

10. Hilkiah was ....
....

11. Horses of the Sun were ....
....

12. Huldah was ....
....

13. Milcom was ....
....

14. Molech was ....
....

15. Nehushtan was ....
....

16. Queen of Heaven was ....
....

17. Shaphan was ....
....

18. Topheth was ....
....

xviii §4.   Number of items adequately stated = ... × 2 = Score.........

Give the information necessary to complete the following account of

ZEPHANIAH

The prophet Zephaniah lived in the .... century B.C. From statements in his book it may be inferred that he was a native of ....'.....
and a descendant of King .... He was a contemporary of the
prophet ....

Prior to the emergence of Zephaniah there had been no great prophet in
Judah since the prophet ...., nearly .... years previously. The reason for such a long period of silence as to prophets probably
was ....
The state of religion in Judah during that long period may be characterized as
one of ...., because Judah's kings, especially King
.... had officially sponsored ....

When Zephaniah began his prophetic career, ... was
King of Judah. The historical event which constitutes the background of his
prophecy was ....,
which occurred in .... B.C. Zephaniah considered that that crisis was
a threat not only to Judah, but also to (1)..............................;
(2)........................; and (3)........................,
as well as other nations. What actually happened to Judah in that crisis was
....
The crisis ended when ....

....

Zephaniah interpreted that crisis as a ....,
a doctrine previously enunciated by the prophets .... and
.... Zephaniah specifically said that it was a
........................, which statement inspired the thirteenth

119

century Christian hymn entitled "......................................,"
                                                23
written by ....
                    24
    Another doctrine which Zephaniah held in common with those two previous prophets (items 20–21) was .... Zephaniah
                                                25
expressed this doctrine as follows: "Seek ye the LORD, all ye ....
..................., who have ....;
                                          26
                    who have ....;
                                27
seek ...., seek ....; it may be that ye
        28   29
will be ...."
                                    30
"I will also leave in the midst of thee ....;
                                                31
and they shall .... in the ....
                        32   33
The .... shall not do ....,
                    34   35
nor ....; neither shall.....................
                36   37
be found in ....; for they shall ....
                        38   39
.... and none shall ...."
                                                40

---

xviii §5a. Number of items adequately stated = ... × 2½ = Score........

120

Give the information necessary to complete the following account of

JEREMIAH

The prophet Jeremiah was of .... lineage. He was a
native of ...., which was located ....
.... within the tribal territory of ....
His prophetic work centered mainly in .... His prophetic
career covered a period of approximately .... years. His call to be a
prophet came in connection with the crisis caused by ....
.... in the year .... B.C., when ....
was King of Judah. After that, his prophetic career spanned four crucial events
in the history of the Hebrews:

(1).......... B.C., when ....
....

(2).......... B.C., when ....
....

(3).......... B.C., when ....
....

(4).......... B.C., when ....
....

We know more about Jeremiah biographically than about any other of the
prophets. This is because ....
....

Some of the personal incidents told about him in this book are:

(1)..
....

(2)..
....

(3) ....
   21
....

(4) ....
   22
....

(5) ....
   23
....

In the popular opinion of Jeremiah's time, religion consisted in ....
   24
....................., and national safety was assured by the fact that

....
   25
Jeremiah said that this opinion was "trusting in lying words," and he cited in

support of his view the historical instance of ....
   26

....

Jeremiah declared that both .... and ....
   27   28
were doomed. For this declaration the priests and the prophets sought to have

Jeremiah executed as a traitor. Jeremiah was saved by the princes and the

people, who cited the historical instance of the prophet ....
   29
who, in the time of King ...., had proclaimed the same
   30
view as Jeremiah, and not only had that historical prophet not been killed but

instead ....
   31

....

Jeremiah held that true religion consists in ....,
   32
and national safety is assured "if ye thoroughly execute ....
   33
between a man and his neighbor."

"Run ye to and fro through the streets of Jerusalem," said Jeremiah, "and

see now, and know, and seek in the broad places thereof, if ye can find ....

......................., if there be any that ....
   34   35
that seeketh ...., and I will ...."
   36   37
Jeremiah even directly challenged the king, saying, "Thus saith the LORD,

(*Continued on Sheet 2*)

Execute ye .... and ...."
  ₃₈   ₃₉

One of the social evils Jeremiah denounced had to do with an injustice to slaves. The law prescribed that ....
  ₄₀

....

This law was violated until an occasion when slave owners became alarmed, when ....
  ₄₁

....

and they liberated their slaves. They subsequently concluded that their fears had been groundless, because ....
  ₄₂

...., and

therefore they rounded up and enslaved them again. Jeremiah denounced this perfidy and said that it would bring upon them ....
  ₄₃

...................., and upon the whole nation ....
  ₄₄

Jeremiah stressed the inwardness of religion. Concerning the inward nature of man, he said, "The heart is ....,
  ₄₅

and it is ....; who can know it?" This in-
  ₄₆

ward need was met by an inward experience of God: "I, the LORD, search ....

................., I try ...., even to give every man
  ₄₇   ₄₈

....,
  ₄₉

according to ...."
  ₅₀

"For I know the thoughts that I think toward you, saith the LORD, thoughts of

................., and not of ...., to give you .....
  ₅₁   ₅₂

....
  ₅₃

Then shall ye call upon me, and ye shall go and ....,
  ₅₄

I will .... And ye shall seek me, and ....
  ₅₅

...................., when ye shall ....
  ₅₆   ₅₇

with all ...." Jeremiah's doctrine of the new covenant
  ₅₈

shows his emphasis upon the inwardness of religion: "Behold, the days come, saith the LORD, that I will make a new covenant with the house of Israel, and

with the house of Jacob; not according to the covenant . . . .
[59]
. . . . in the day that

. . . .
[60]
. . . ., which my covenant they broke, although I

was a . . . . unto them, saith the LORD. But this shall be
[61]
the covenant that I will make with the house of Israel: After those days, saith

the LORD, I will . . . . and write
[62]
it in their . . . . and I will be
[63]
. . . . and they shall . . . . "
[64]   [65]
Jeremiah's creative contribution to Hebrew thinking was the doctrine of

. . . . This new doctrine
[66]
contradicted the conventional doctrine of . . . .
[67]
Said Jeremiah, "In those days they shall say no more, The fathers . . . .
[68]
. . . . and the . . . .
[69]
. . . . But every one shall . . . .
[70]
. . . .; every man that . . . .
[71]
his . . . ."
[72]
Some striking moral attributes of God which Jeremiah preached are seen in

his sayings: "Wilt thou not from this time cry unto me, ...
[73]
. . . . thou art . . . .?"
[74]
"I am the LORD who exercise . . . ., ...
[75]   [76]
and . . . . in the earth, for in these things I delight,
[77]
saith the LORD." "The LORD appeared of old unto me, saying, Yea I . . . .
[78]
. . . .;

therefore with . . . . have I drawn thee."
[79]
As an author, Jeremiah ranks high. Like most of the great prophets, much

that he wrote is in the form of . . . . He used choice meta-
[80]

(*Continued on Sheet 3*)

124

phors; for example, "Can the .... change his ....,
₈₁   ₈₂

or the .... his ....? then may ye also
       ₈₃   ₈₄

.... that are accustomed to ...."
  ₈₅   ₈₆

One of the interesting features of Jeremiah's writings is his use of parables.

Some of his parables are (1)...................................;
                                              ₈₇

(2)..........................; (3)..............................
      ₈₈   ₈₉

One notable letter which Jeremiah wrote is preserved in his book. It was written

probably in the year .... and was sent to ....
                      ₉₀   ₉₁

.... urging them to ....
                                                  ₉₂

.... because ....
                                      ₉₃

....

Jeremiah dictated his sermons to his scribe ....
                                                  ₉₄

On a dramatic occasion this scribe read the book (which was in the form of

....................) to King .... What the king did
  ₉₅   ₉₆

with this book was ....
                                          ₉₇

After this Jeremiah ....
                                      ₉₈

The final sermons which Jeremiah preached were given in ....
                                                            ₉₉

to ....
                      ₁₀₀

Jeremiah died in that place, possibly a martyr.

xviii §5b.   Number of items adequately stated = Score..........

Give the information necessary to complete the following account of

HABAKKUK

The prophet Habakkuk lived in the .... century B.C. Biographical
₁
details are not known. He was a contemporary of the prophet ....
₂

The historical situation which constituted the background of his prophecy
was the critical period which followed ....
..............................., when Judah came under the overlordship
₃
of ....
₄

A century before Habakkuk's time the prophet .... had said
₅
that God raised up the oppressor nation .... to be
₆
.... So now the crisis in
₇
Habakkuk's time was interpreted: "O LORD, thou has ordained them for ......
.................; and thou, O .... hast established
₈   ₉
them for ...." Habakkuk challenged this doctrine and said;
₁₀
"Thou art of .... than to ....,
₁₁   ₁₂
and canst not ....;
₁₃
wherefore .... them that ....,
₁₄   ₁₅
and .... when ....
₁₆   ₁₇
.... the man that is ....?" Then
₁₈
Habakkuk said, "I will stand upon my ...., and set me upon
₁₉
......................................, and will look to see ....
₂₀   ₂₁
.... and what I shall
..............,.... concerning .... And the LORD answered
₂₂   ₂₃
me, and said, Write .... and make it plain upon
₂₄
..........................., that he may ....
₂₅   ₂₆
.... For the .... is yet for ......
₂₇   ₂₈
......................, and it hastens ....
₂₉

.... and will ....;
                                    30
though it ...., ...;
              31   32
because it will ...., it will not ...."
                  33   34
The statement for which Habakkuk is most famous is: "The ....
                                                        35
shall ....," a doctrine basic to the
                              36
theology of St. Paul and of the Protestant Reformation.

Habakkuk set forth the view that the true life of the upright man is not in outward circumstances or material prosperity, in a splendid passage: "Though .... shall not ....
                    37   38
Neither shall ....;
                                39
The labor of ....;
                          40
And the .... yield ....;
                  41   42
The .... shall be ....,
            43   44
And there shall be .... in the ....;
                          45   46
Yet I will .... in ....,
                    47   48
I will .... in the ...."
                49   50

xviii §5c.   Number of items adequately stated = ... × 2 = Score........

128

Who said it?

1. "For I desire mercy, and not sacrifice; and the knowledge of God more than burnt-offerings."

....1

2. "Holy, holy, holy is the LORD of hosts; the whole earth is full of his glory."

....2

3. "Seek good, and not evil, that you may live; and so the LORD, the God of hosts, will be with you, as you have said. Hate the evil, and love the good, and establish justice in the gate; perhaps the LORD, the God of hosts, will be gracious unto the remnant of Joseph."

....3

4. "Seek the LORD, all ye meek of the earth, who have kept his ordinances; seek uprightness, seek humility; it may be you will be hid in the day of the LORD's anger."

....4

5. "The fathers shall not be put to death for the children, neither shall the children be put to death for the fathers; every man shall be put to death for his own sin."

....5

6. "The heart is deceitful above all things, and it is desperately corrupt; who can know it? I, the LORD, search the mind, I test the heart, to reward every man according to his ways, according to the fruit of his doings."

....6

7. "The just shall live by his faith."

....7

8. "This is the covenant that I will make with the house of Israel: After those days, saith the LORD, I will put my law in their inward parts, and write it in their hearts; and will be their God, and they shall be my people. And they shall teach no more every man his neighbor, and every man his brother, saying, Know the LORD; for they shall all know me, from the least of them unto the greatest of them, saith the LORD; for I will forgive their iniquity, and I will remember their sin no more."

....8

9. "Wash you, make you clean; put away the evil of your doings from before mine eyes; cease to do evil; learn to do well; make justice your aim, relieve the oppressed, judge the fatherless, plead for the widow. Come now, and let us reason together, saith the LORD; though your sins be as scarlet, they

shall be as white as snow; though they be red like crimson, they shall be as wool."

...............................9

10. "Wherewith shall I come before the LORD, and bow myself before the high God? shall I come before him with burnt-offerings, with calves a year old? will the LORD be pleased with thousands of rams, or with ten thousands of rivers of oil? shall I give my firstborn for my transgression, the fruit of my body for the sin of my soul? He hath showed thee, O man, what is good; and what doth the LORD require of thee, but to do justly, and to love mercy, and to walk humbly with thy God?"

...............................10

xviii. Number of items correctly answered = ... × 10 = Score.........

130

Number each item in the second column to correspond with that word in the first column with which it is correctly associated.

<table>
<tr><td>1. Amel-Marduk</td><td>( ) Center of Cyrus the Great's power in the west</td></tr>
<tr><td>2. Ammonites</td><td>( ) First religious festival observed by repatriated Jewish</td></tr>
<tr><td>3. Anshan</td><td>exiles</td></tr>
<tr><td>4. Arabah</td><td></td></tr>
<tr><td>5. Artaxerxes</td><td>( ) Foreigners who crowded the Edomites out of their</td></tr>
<tr><td>6. Belshazzar</td><td>ancestral home</td></tr>
<tr><td>7. Cambyses</td><td>( ) Foreigners who settled in southern Judah after the</td></tr>
<tr><td>8. Chebar</td><td>exile began</td></tr>
<tr><td>9. Croesus</td><td></td></tr>
<tr><td>10. Darius</td><td>( ) Jewish concept of their own true type of political</td></tr>
<tr><td>11. Dispersion</td><td>organization</td></tr>
<tr><td>12. Elam</td><td></td></tr>
<tr><td>13. Elephantiné</td><td>( ) Jewish king who was a prisoner for 37 years</td></tr>
<tr><td>14. Ezekiel</td><td>( ) Jews outside Palestine in the Mediterranean area,</td></tr>
<tr><td>15. Firman</td><td>especially Egypt</td></tr>
<tr><td>16. Haggai</td><td>( ) King who added Egypt to the Persian Empire</td></tr>
<tr><td>17. Hophra</td><td>( ) King who exiled the Jews</td></tr>
<tr><td>18. Idumeans</td><td></td></tr>
<tr><td>19. Jehoiachin</td><td>( ) Last king of the Chaldean Empire</td></tr>
<tr><td>20. Jehoiakim</td><td>( ) Leader of first repatriated Jewish exiles</td></tr>
<tr><td>21. Jeremiah</td><td>( ) Persian king who appointed Nehemiah as governor</td></tr>
<tr><td>22. Joshua</td><td>of Jerusalem</td></tr>
<tr><td>23. Labashi-Marduk</td><td></td></tr>
<tr><td>24. Media</td><td>( ) Persian royal decree</td></tr>
<tr><td>25. Nabateans</td><td>( ) Prophet who urged the Jews to finish the rebuilding</td></tr>
<tr><td>26. Nabonidus</td><td>of the Jerusalem temple</td></tr>
<tr><td>27. Nebuchadrezzar</td><td></td></tr>
<tr><td>28. Nergal-sharezer</td><td>( ) Prophet who was an exile</td></tr>
<tr><td>29. Petra</td><td>( ) Prophet who wrote a letter to the Jewish exiles</td></tr>
<tr><td>30. Samaritans</td><td>( ) Site of a colony of Jewish exiles in Babylonia</td></tr>
<tr><td>31. Sardis</td><td>( ) Site of a colony of Jewish refugees in Egypt</td></tr>
<tr><td>32. Tabernacles</td><td></td></tr>
<tr><td>33. Tattenai</td><td>( ) Son of the last king of Chaldea, better known than</td></tr>
<tr><td>34. Teima</td><td>his father</td></tr>
<tr><td>35. Tell Abib</td><td>( ) Where Cyrus first rose to political power</td></tr>
<tr><td>36. Theocracy</td><td></td></tr>
<tr><td>37. Xerxes</td><td></td></tr>
<tr><td>38. Zechariah</td><td></td></tr>
<tr><td>39. Zedekiah</td><td></td></tr>
<tr><td>40. Zerubbabel</td><td></td></tr>
</table>

xix §§1–2. Number of items correctly numbered = ... × 5 = Score.......

Who or what were the following?

1. Anathbethel: ....
....

2. Apsu: ....
....

3. Assuan: ....
....

4. Bel: ....
....

5. Borsippa: ....
....

6. Chebar: ....
....

7. Elephantiné: ....
....

8. Enuma Elish: ....
....

9. Ezida: ....
....

10. Haggai: ....
....

11. Joshua: ....
....

12. Marduk: ....
....

13. Nebo: ....
....

14. Nehemiah: ....
....

15. Nubia: ....
....

16. So: ....
....

17. Tiamat: ....
....

18. Yahu: ....
....

19. Zechariah: ....
....

20. Zerubbabel: ....
....

xix §3. Number of adequate statements = ... × 5 = Score..........

On each blank line insert a topic appropriate to that part of

THE GENESIS CREATION EPIC

Prologue: ....

<table>
<tr><td>Canto I</td><td>Canto II</td></tr>
</table>

Canto I	Canto II
The First Order of Creation	*The Second Order of Creation*
I	IV
And God said:	*And God said:*
....	....
And God saw that it was good	*And God saw that it was good*
And there was evening,	*And there was evening,*
and there was morning, Day I	*and there was morning,* Day IV
II	V
And God said:	*And God said:*
....	....
	And God saw that it was good
And there was evening,	*And there was evening,*
and there was morning, Day II	*and there was morning,* Day V
III	VI
And God said:	*And God said:*
....	....
And God saw that it was good	*And God saw that it was good*
And God said:	*And God said:*
....	....
(Consummation of the First Order)	(Consummation of the Second Order)
And God saw that it was good	*And God saw that it was very good*
And there was evening,	*And there was evening,*
and there was morning, Day III	*and there was morning,* Day VI

Epilogue: .... Day VII

xix §3(b3).   Number of adequate statements = ... × 10 = Score........

Give the information necessary to complete the following.

The canonical Old Testament books which probably originated in the two centuries immediately following the destruction of Jerusalem are

1. .... 2. .... 3. ....
4. .... 5. .... 6. ....
7. .... 8. .... 9. ....

State in which one of these books you would look to find:

10. "Against the Shepherds of Israel" ....
11. "And ye shall be holy unto me, for I, the LORD, am holy, and have set you apart from the peoples, that ye should be mine" ....
12. "Behold, I send my messenger, and he shall prepare the way before me; and the LORD, whom ye seek, will suddenly come to his temple".............
13. "Finish the Temple" ....
14. "Individual Moral Responsibility" ....
15. "The Doom of Edom" ....
16. "The Eagles and the Vine" ....
17. "The Glory of the New Jerusalem" ....
18. "The LORD Treading the Winepress" ....
19. "The Rehabilitation of Jerusalem" ....
20. "The Suffering Servant" ....
21. "The Valley of Dry Bones" ....
22. "The Vision of the Four Creatures and the Wheels" ....
23. "The Wreck of the Good Ship Tyre" ....
24. "Thou shalt love thy neighbor as thyself" ....
25. "Threnodies on the Fall of Jerusalem" ....

xix §4. Number of items correctly stated = ... × 4 = Score..........

Who or what were the following?

1. Atonement: ....
....
2. Booths: ....
....
3. Canon: ....
....
4. Ingathering: ....
....
5. Jubilee: ....
....
6. Levites: ....
....
7. Libation: ....
....
8. Nisan: ....
....
9. Passover: ....
....
10. Pentateuch: ....
....
11. Pentecost: ....
....
12. Rosh Hashanah: ....
....
13. Shema: ....
....
14. Showbread: ....
....
15. Tabernacles: ....
....
16. Targum: ....
....
17. Tishri: ....
....
18. Trumpets: ....
....
19. Unleavened Bread: ....
....
20. Yom Kippur: ....
....

xix §5.   Number of adequate statements = ... × 5 = Score..........

NAME_____ Date_____ Score_____ **59**

xix

Give the information necessary to complete the following statements about

THE TORAH

1. The source documents which make up the Torah are:

Symbol	Title	Date of origin	Place of origin
(1).........	....	....	....
(2).........	....	....	....
(3).........	....	....	....
(4).........	....	....	....

The probable successive steps in the process of their combination were:

(1)...... was combined with ...... to form ...... sometime after .....

(2)...... was combined with ...... to form ...... sometime after .....

(3)...... was combined with ...... to form ...... probably about.....

2. The word Torah means .... Other names for the Torah are (1)...................., a word which means ....; (2)...........................

3. The Bible books which make up the Torah are ....

4. The first portion of the Torah which was canonized was .... This happened about the year .... in [place] ...., on the occasion of .... Two important persons connected with this event were (1)................ and (2).................... The biblical account of that occasion is in the book of ....

5. A later and more important occasion connected with the canonization of (most likely the entire) Torah occurred about the year .... in [place] .... on the occasion of .... Two important persons connected with this event were (1)........................ (2)........................ The biblical account of that occasion is in the book of ....

xix §§4–5. Number of items adequately stated = ... × 2 = Score........

Give the information necessary to complete the following statements.

1. By the Samaritan Schism is meant ....
   ....
   It occurred shortly before ....
   .... The basic causes of it were
   (1)..
   (2)..
   (3)..
   It led to the building of ....
2. Hellenism means the spread of ....
   and its ....
3. After the death of Alexander the Great, his empire was divided among
   ...., chiefly ....
   Palestine was principally under the rule of ....
   until 198 B.C.; local governmental affairs of the Jews in Jerusalem were in
   charge of an official known as the .... Associated with
   this official was a body (of officials) known as the ....;
   this body was the forerunner of the Jewish governing body in later centuries
   called the ....
4. Hierocracy means ....
5. After 198 B.C., Palestine was under the rule of ....
6. In the third century B.C., the everyday language of Palestinian Jews was
   ....; the everyday language of other Jews (excepting those
   in Babylon) was ....
7. Diaspora means ....
8. Gerizim is ....

Number each item in the second column to correspond with that word in the first column with which it is correctly associated.

1. Ahura Mazda
2. Angels
3. Angra-Mainyu
4. Ascents
5. Ben-Sira
6. Book of the Twelve
7. Canonization
8. Demons
9. Dualism
10. Festivals
11. Habakkuk
12. Haggai
13. Hagiographa
14. Hallelujah
15. Hasidim
16. Idolatry
17. Isaiah
18. Jeremiah
19. Joel
20. Johanan
21. Jonah
22. Joshua
23. Judges
24. Kings
25. Legalism
26. Liturgy
27. Malachi
28. Micah
29. Monism
30. Monotheism
31. Nahum
32. Obadiah
33. Prophets
34. Ritual
35. Sacrifice
36. Sages
37. Satan
38. Scribes
39. Transcendence
40. Torah

( ) A group of pilgrim songs in the Psalter

( ) Author of Ecclesiasticus

( ) Collection of Jewish Scriptures canonized about 200 B.C.

( ) Devoutly earnest devotees of Judaism, ardent opponents of Hellenism

( ) Doctrine that God is above and beyond all other beings

( ) Doctrine that there are two ultimate realities, which are antithetical

( ) Doctrine that there is only one ultimate reality

( ) One of the Former Prophets

( ) Persian good god, or god of light.

( ) Pre-eminent feature of temple worship

( ) Prescribed forms for public worship

( ) Process by which books came to rate as Holy Scripture

( ) Professional students of the Jewish Sacred Scriptures

( ) "Save, Lord"

( ) Supernatural intermediaries between God and man

( ) Supreme evil power in Persian religion

( ) "The Adversary"

( ) The Written Law

( ) Third division of Jewish Holy Scriptures

( ) Wisdom teachers of Judaism

---

xx §4.   Number of items correctly numbered = ... × 5 = Score.........

Give the information necessary to complete the following statements.

1. Septuagint is ....
2. An Old Testament book which may be classed as an essay is ....
3. An Old Testament book which may be classed as a short story is ....
4. Old Testament books which may be classed as "Wisdom Literature" are

   ....
5. Canonical Old Testament books which probably originated in the fourth and third centuries B.C. are ....

   ....

   ....

6. In what Old Testament book would you look to find each of the following?

   (1) "When I consider thy heavens, the work of thy fingers,
   The moon and the stars, which thou hast ordained;
   What is man, that thou art mindful of him?
   And the son of man, that thou visitest him?
   For thou hast made him but little less than God,
   And hast crowned him with glory and honor."

   ....(1)

   (2) "Happy is the man that findeth wisdom,
   And the man that getteth understanding.
   For the profit of it is better than the profit of silver,
   And the gain thereof than fine gold."

   ....(2)

   (3) "I know that my Redeemer liveth,
   And hereafter he will stand upon the earth.
   And when after my skin this body is destroyed,
   Without my flesh I shall see God;
   Whom I shall see on my side,
   And mine eyes shall see, no longer a stranger.
   My heart is spent within me."

   ....(3)

   (4) "What has been is what shall be; and what has been done is what shall be done; and there is no new thing under the sun."

   ....(4)

   (5) "Many waters cannot quench love,
   Nor can floods drown it;
   If a man would offer all the substance of his house for love,
   It would be utterly contemned."

   ....(5)

(6) "Proclaim ye this among the nations: prepare war; stir up the mighty men; let all the men of war draw near, let them come up. Beat your plowshares into swords, and your pruning-hooks into spears; . . . let the nations rouse themselves, and come up to the valley of Jehoshaphat; for there will I sit to judge all the nations on every side."

...........(6)

(7) "I knew that thou art a gracious God, and merciful, slow to anger, and of great kindness, and repentest thee of the evil. Therefore now, O LORD, take, I beseech thee, my life from me; for it is better for me to die than to live."

............(7)

xx §5. Number of items correctly stated = ... × 4 = Score..........

Number each item in the second column to correspond with that word in the first column with which it is correctly associated.

1. Alexandra
2. Alexandria
3. Antigonus
4. Antiochus III
5. Antiochus IV
6. Antipater
7. Antony
8. Aretas
9. Augustus
10. Ben-Shetach
11. Cassius
12. Crassus
13. Epiphanes
14. Gerizim
15. Gerousia
16. Hanukkah
17. Hasidim
18. Hasmoneans
19. Hellenism
20. Herod
21. Hyrcanus I
22. Hyrcanus II
23. Jason
24. John Hyrcanus
25. Jonathan
26. Mariamme
27. Mattathias
28. Menelaus
29. Modein
30. Nicanor
31. Octavian
32. Onias
33. Pharisees
34. Phasael
35. Pompey
36. Sadducees
37. Sanhedrin
38. Scaurus
39. Simon
40. Zadok

( ) Accepted both written and oral Jewish law

( ) Another name for the Maccabean rulers

( ) Appointed Herod as king of the Jews

( ) Became ethnarch of Judea when the Romans took over the country

( ) Culture pattern not acceptable to orthodox Jews

( ) First Jewish ruler to issue coins

( ) Governor of Galilee who later became procurator of all Syria

( ) Honorific name of the grandson of Antiochus the Great

( ) Jewish Feast of the Dedication

( ) Jewish high priest

( ) Jewish priest who precipitated the Maccabean war

( ) Jewish queen

( ) National Jewish leader after the death of Judas Maccabeus

( ) Predecessors of the Pharisees

( ) Roman who plundered the Jerusalem temple

( ) Syrian general defeated by Judas Maccabeus

( ) The high-priestly group in New Testament times

( ) The Senate of Jerusalem

( ) Where the Samaritan temple was located

( ) Wife of King Herod the Great

xxi.   Number of items correctly numbered = ... × 5 = Score..........

Indicate the classification of each of the following books by a check mark in the appropriate column.

	Canonical	Apoc-ryphal	Pseudepi-graphical
1. Antiquities of the Jews............			
2. Aristeas			
3. I Baruch			
4. II Baruch			
5. Bel and the Dragon............			
6. Book of the Twelve............			
7. Daniel			
8. Ecclesiastes			
9. Ecclesiasticus			
10. I Enoch			
11. II Enoch			
12. I Esdras			
13. II Esdras			
14. Esther			
15. Ezra			
16. IV Ezra			
17. Hagiographa			
18. History of Susanna			
19. Jashar			
20. Jewish War			
21. Jubilees			
22. Judges			
23. Judith			
24. Kethubim			
25. Koheleth			
26. Life of Josephus...........			
27. I Maccabees			
28. II Maccabees			
29. III Maccabees			
30. IV Maccabees			
31. Nahum			
32. Obadiah			
33. Pentateuch			
34. Philo....................			
35. Pirke Aboth			
36. Prayer of Manasses.........			

	Canonical	Apocryphal	Pseudepigraphical
37. Proverbs of Solomon.............			
38. Psalms of David..................			
39. Psalms of Solomon...............			
40. Sayings of the Jewish Fathers.......			
41. Sibylline Oracles			
42. Sira			
43. Song of Solomon.................			
44. Song of Songs...................			
45. Testaments of the Twelve Patriarchs..			
46. The Three Holy Children.........			
47. Tobit			
48. Treatise Against Apion...........			
49. Wisdom of Solomon..............			
50. Zechariah			

xxii. Number of items correctly checked = ... × 2 = Score..........

In what Jewish book would you look to find the following?

1. An account of the translation of the Septuagint.

..................................1

2. "And now, my children, I exhort you, love each one his brother, and put away hatred from your hearts; love one another in deed, and in word, and in the inclination of the soul. . . . Love one another from the heart; and if a man sin against thee, speak peaceably to him, and in thy soul hold not guile; and if he repent and confess, forgive him. . . . And though he deny it and yet have a sense of shame when reproved, give over reproving him. For he who denies may repent so as not again to wrong thee; yea, he may also honor thee, and be at peace with thee. And if he be shameless and persist in his wrongdoing, even so forgive him from the heart, and leave to God the avenging."

..................................2

3. "Behold, O Lord, and raise up unto them their king, the son of David,
   At the time in which thou seest, O God, that he may reign over Israel thy
     servant. . . .
   And he shall gather together a holy people, whom he shall lead in righteous-
     ness.
   And he shall judge the tribes of the people that has been sanctified by the
     Lord his God.
   And he shall not suffer unrighteousness to lodge any more in their midst,
     Nor shall there dwell with them any man that knoweth wickedness,
     For he shall know them, that they are all sons of their God. . . .
   All nations shall be in fear before him,
     For he will smite the earth with the word of his mouth for ever.
   He will bless the people of the Lord with wisdom and gladness,
     And he himself will be pure from sin, so that he may rule a great people.
   He will rebuke rulers, and remove sinners by the might of his word."

..................................3

4. Essay on Physicians.

..................................4

5. "For in the memory of virtue is immortality, because it is recognized both before God and before men; when it is present men imitate it, and they long after it when it is departed; and throughout all time it marcheth crowned in triumph, victorious in the strife for the prizes that are undefiled."

..................................5

6. History, from creation to Covenant at Sinai, told in fifty-year periods.

..................................6

7. "In Praise of Famous Men"

..................................7

8. "In thee do we trust, for lo! thy law is with us, and we know that we shall not fail so long as we keep thy statutes."

..................................8

9. "Our works are subject to our own choice and power
    To do right or wrong in the works of our hands;
    And in thy righteousness thou visitest the sons of men.
  He that doeth righteousness layeth up life for himself with the Lord;
    And he that doeth wrongly forfeits his life to destruction."
 9

10. "Rejoice greatly, O daughter of Zion; shout, O daughter of Jerusalem; behold,
    thy king cometh unto thee; he is just, and having salvation; lowly, and riding
    on an ass, on a colt the foal of an ass. And I will cut off the chariot from
    Ephraim, and the horse from Jerusalem; and the battle bow shall be cut off;
    and he shall speak peace to the nations; and his dominion shall be from sea
    to sea, and from the River to the ends of the earth."
 10

11. The Beheading of Holofernes.
 11

12. The coming of Messiah, the resurrection, and the judgment.
 12

13. "The day is short and the work is great, and the laborers are slow, and the hire
    is much, and the master of the house is urgent. It is not incumbent on thee to
    finish the work, and thou art not free to desist from it. If thou hast learned
    much Torah, they will give thee much hire; and the master of thy work is
    faithful who will pay thee the hire of thy labor; and know that the giving of the
    reward of the righteous is for the time to come."
 13

14. The handwriting on the wall.
 14

15. The alleged predictions of a Greek prophetess about the greatness of the Jews.
 15

16. The story of Nebuchadrezzar's golden image.
 16

17. The three Hebrews in the fiery furnace.
 17

18. "To whom ought a man to show liberality? All men acknowledge that we
    ought to show liberality to those who are well disposed towards us, but I think
    we ought to show the same keen spirit of generosity to those who are opposed
    to us that by this means we may win them over to the right and to what is
    advantageous to ourselves."
 18

19. "What is the teaching of wisdom? As you wish that no evil should befall you,
    but to be a partaker of all good things, so you should act on the same principle
    towards your subjects and offenders, and you should mildly admonish the noble
    and good. For God draws all men to himself by his benignity."
 19

20. "What you hate, to no one do."
 20

xxii. Number of items correctly stated = ... ✕ 5 = Score. . . . .

Give the information necessary to complete the following account of

JESUS OF NAZARETH

Now when Jesus was born in .... about the year
.... the Jews of Palestine were under the rule of a king named
.... This man's kingdom was, however, under
the overlordship of ...., as indeed all Palestine had been
since the year .... This king died in the year .... and
his kingdom was then divided among .... of his sons. One of these
sons, named ...., was given the title of ethnarch
and ruled over .... Another son, whose name was
.... and whose title was ....
was ruler over that part of Palestine where Jesus spent most of his life, namely
....

One of the Gospels states that Jesus was about .... years of age
when he began his public career. Prior to his public career he lived in the village of .... The Gospels give the names of his parents as
.... and ...., and the names of
.... brothers as ....
.... and further
state that he also had sisters, but their names are not given. Jesus' parents seem
to have been devoutly religious people, doubtless of that type often referred to
as the ....

In his native village Jesus had certain advantages of elementary schooling
at the local .... Beyond that he appears to
have had no formal education, but during his formative years he would have
been helped in developing his religious experience and thinking (1) by occa-
sional contact with visiting .... teachers, who met with
small groups both out of doors and in private homes; (2) by regular weekly
attendance on the .... day at the religious services
in the ...., where he would hear the Scriptures read
and explained. Now in Jesus' lifetime the Jewish Sacred Scriptures included
the books which make up what they called the .... and the
......................., but not all of the books in the canonical group
now known as the .... were then regarded as Sacred
Scripture. These Jewish Sacred Scriptures were written in the ....
.... language, but during Jesus' lifetime plain people did
not understand that language any more, and therefore at the ....
.... services the selections were read in the original and
then a translation was given in the vernacular language, which was ....

.... (3) A third formative influence for Jesus was, of course, his own private reading, not only of the Sacred Books, but of other non-canonical (which means ....
....
.............) books, of which one of the most interesting is the book called
....,
a book which then held a place in devout religious circles comparable to that which *Pilgrim's Progress* once held in America.

Prior to his public career Jesus worked at his trade as a ....
..................., not only in his native village but quite possibly also in the neighboring city of ...., which lay four miles to the north, where an extensive building program was in progress during Jesus' young manhood. This city was the largest city in all ....
and was the capital of .... until that ruler built a new capital city on the shore of ...., which city he named .... in honor of the emperor. Working thus in this large neighboring city would have brought Jesus many diversified social contacts, especially with ...., who spoke the .... language, but whether Jesus understood and used that language is a matter of conjecture.

Throughout Jesus' lifetime there was a great deal of unrest among the Jews, due to the fact that they resented the .... overlordship and wished for political independence again. When Jesus was about twelve years of age, that is, in the year ...., there was a good deal of disturbance. The ruler of one of the major divisions of Palestine had proved to be such a tyrant and so offensive to the Jews that they asked the emperor to depose him. Apparently the Jews assumed that another son of ....
.... would succeed to the rule of the deposed
..........................., but instead, the emperor placed ....
.... under the administration of an official called a
........................, who was directly responsible to the emperor himself. Some Jews were not reconciled to this; such Jews made up that political faction which in the Gospels is called ....
In connection with this overturn, a census was instituted which, of course, was with a view to the taxation of the Jews. Jewish resentment was so strong that an attempt at revolution was made in the area called ....,
under the leadership of Judas of Gamala and a Pharisee named Sadduk. The outbreak was put down, but the spirit of revolution lived on in the party called
.... (which is the same
as ....). This is of interest in connection with the life of Jesus both because of where this revolutionary party originated, and because one of Jesus' disciples, named ....,

(*Continued on Sheet 2*)

may have belonged to this revolutionary party. This faction believed that the only way the Jews would ever have their freedom again was to fight for it, and ultimately this faction did precipitate the Jewish War, which brought about the total destruction of Jerusalem by .... in the year .... The story of this Jewish War is told by the Jewish historian ....

During Jesus' lifetime the Jews deeply resented the taxes to which they were subjected. This was because .... The general method employed in tax collection was that known as ...., which means that collectors (1)....................................... .... and (2)... .... In the Gospels the term for tax collector is .... Included among the disciples of Jesus was a tax collector named .... At one time in his career certain of his foes tried to get Jesus into trouble over the subject of taxes by asking him, "... ....?" [2] Jesus replied in the oft-quoted statement, "................................ ...." [2] Jesus' introduction to a public career came in connection with a popular movement inaugurated by ...., to which movement Jesus attached himself by submitting to the rite of .... This was an occasion of profound personal religious experience for Jesus, the heart of the experience being stated, "And lo, a voice from heaven, saying ...." [2] Directly following this incident the Gospels recount the story of Jesus' .... of which there were three phases: (1)... (2)... (3)... The Gospels indicate that Jesus began his own public career after .... The greater part of the public work of Jesus was performed in .... During this ministry he made his headquarters at the city of ...., which was located ...., perhaps at the home there of one of his disciples named .... An interesting incident which took place in that home was ....

161

Jesus' public career was preëminently that of a teacher. One of the best known groupings of his teachings is the Sermon on the Mount, which is found in the Gospel according to .... A suitable title for this sermon, giving some indication of the nature of its contents, is .... [2] Some of the significant teachings in this sermon are: "Blessed are the poor in spirit, for ...."

"Blessed are the ...., for they shall inherit the earth."

"Blessed are the ...., for they shall see God."

"Let your light so ....

....

...." [2]

"You have heard that it has been said, 'An eye for an eye, and a tooth for a tooth.' But I say unto you, ...

....

...." [2]

"You have heard that it has been said, 'You must love your neighbor, and ....' but I say unto you, ...

....

....

...." [3]

"But when you pray, enter ....

....

....

...." [3]

"Do not worry about your life, what ....,

nor about your ....

Is not the life more than .... and the ....

....?"

"But seek ....

....

...." [3]

Jesus regarded one of his teachings in the Sermon on the Mount as of such great importance that he said of it, "This is the law and the prophets"; that teaching is, "..

....

...." [2]

One of the striking features of Jesus' teaching method was his use of the parable. Now parable may be explained as ....

....

....

(*Continued on Sheet 3*)

One of the important topics in the teaching of Jesus was "The Kingdom of God," which he illustrated by several parables, which usually begin, "Now the kingdom of God (or, heaven) is like." Some examples of such parables are

(1) ....

(2) ....

(3) ....

(4) ....

(5) ....

Of these parables, the one which interests me most runs in detail as follows:

....

....

....

....

....

....

....

....

.... [5]

This parable seems to indicate that by the Kingdom of God Jesus meant ......

....

....

....

....

....

....

....

....

.... [5]

Certain of the teachings of Jesus are characterized as apocalyptical, or eschatological. Apocalyptic means literally .... and designates (1) ....

(2) ....

(3) ....

Eschatology means ....

It is a phase of .... and deals with

....

Apocalyptic is basically concerned with two ethical problems, (1) ....

....

(2) ....

163

Jesus illustrated his eschatological ideas in parables. One example of such is the parable of the ....
In detail this parable runs as follows: ....
....
....
....
....
....
....
....
....
.... [5]
The central idea in eschatology is that of the Judgment. In the teaching of Jesus the ethical significance of the idea of the Judgment is ....
....
....
....
....
....
....
....
.... [5]

In connection with several of the mighty works of Jesus, faith is emphasized. An example is ....
....
....
On the basis of this, as well as other examples, faith may be interpreted to mean
....
....
....
.... [3]

Considering the teaching of Jesus as a whole, some interpreters find the keynote of his teaching in the meaning of the word "Jesus," which is ....
....
A parable of Jesus which clearly portrays this keynote is the parable of ....
....
An incident of Jesus' ministry which clearly portrays this keynote is the story of
....
....
....

The career of Jesus ended in martyrdom. There were several causes for this. For one thing, Jesus was accused of ....
An incident in his career which was made a basis for this accusation was ......

(*Continued on Sheet 4*)

. . . .

. . . .

For another thing, Jesus was accused of . . . .
An incident in his career which was made a basis for this accusation was

. . . .

. . . .

Again, Jesus was accused of . . . .
An incident in his career which was made a basis for this accusation was . . . . . .

. . . .

. . . .

Yet again, Jesus was accused of . . . .
An incident in his career which was made a basis for this accusation was . . . . . .

. . . .

. . . .

Many of the events in the last week of Jesus' life took place at the temple in
Jerusalem. Now this temple is known historically as the temple of . . . .
. . . . because . . . .

. . . .

. . . .

The temple building contained two rooms. The main entrance, located on the
. . . . side of the building, opened into a room called . . . .
. . . . The inner room was called
. . . . ; this inner room contained

. . . .

Surrounding the building were several courts. The court closest to the temple
building was the Court of . . . . ;
the court next beyond that was the Court of . . . . ;
the court next beyond that was the Court of . . . . ,
so called because . . . .

. . . . ;

beyond that was the outermost court, known as the Court of . . . .
. . . . In this outermost court occurred one of
the most dramatic events of Jesus' career, namely, ...

. . . .

Jesus was betrayed into the hands of his enemies by one of his own disciples
named . . . . The betrayal took place in
. . . . , which was located on the

. . . .

After being arrested, Jesus was taken for examination before the Jewish court
known as the . . . . which was a body numbering . . . .
composed of representatives of the two outstanding religious parties of the time,

namely the .... and the ....
They judged Jesus to be worthy of death on the charge of ....
But they did not have the authority to condemn him to death and therefore
they had to secure his condemnation from the political official called the
.... The name of this official was ....
.... The charge made against Jesus before this official was ...., which was not the same as
the charge on which the Jewish court condemned him. Jesus was sentenced to
death. The method of his execution was .... The
place where the execution occurred was called ....,
near the city of .... The day of the week on which
Jesus was executed was .... It happened at the time of year
when the Jews were observing the Feast of the ....
Jesus was buried in a tomb which belonged to ....
On the .... day after the crucifixion occurred the resurrection,
which is celebrated in the preëminent Christian festival of ....

During his public ministry Jesus was attended by disciples. They are commonly understood to have been .... in number, but the Gospel according to Luke speaks of a larger group of .... in number, and several
times mention is made of "the multitude of his disciples." Among his disciples
there was a select inner circle of .... in number, namely ....
....

The disciples were personally devoted to Jesus and they sought to understand his significance. On one occasion, "When Jesus came into the area of
Caesarea Philippi he asked his disciples saying, Who do folks say that the Son
of Man is? They said, Some say John the Baptist; some, Elijah; and others
Jeremiah, or one of the .... He said unto them, But who
say you that I am? And .... answered and said, You are
....
....
...." [2]
This confession is at the heart of the Christian faith.

xxiv. Number of items adequately stated = ... × ½ = Score.........

166

Give the information necessary to complete the following account of

EARLY CHRISTIAN ORGANIZATION

Before the term Christian was coined, the early Christians were known by
a variety of names. They were called ....;

.............................; ....;

             2   3

.............................; ....;

             4   5

.............................;

             6   7

The name Christian originated in .... It means

                                   8

.... The Greek word "Christ" means

                         9

.... and corresponds to the Jewish term

                        10

....

             11

The first apostles were the former twelve disciples of Jesus, excepting Judas
Iscariot, whose place was filled by ....

                       12

The special ministry of the apostles was (1)................................

                       13

and (2)...

                  14

The term apostle means ....

                       15

The qualifications of an apostle were (1)....................................

                                  16

.... and

(2)..

                  17

Paul deemed himself fully qualified to be an apostle because ....

                       18

....

Christian prophets concerned themselves principally with ....

                       19

.... The book of ....

                       20

is the preëminent example of such prophesying. The author of this book is regarded as a "seer," which means ....

                       21

....

The chief function of Christian teachers most likely was to instruct Chris-

tians in . . . .
22

A Christian evangelist was . . . .
23

The Greek term for elder is . . . . The function of elders in
24

a Christian group was . . . .
25

In time pastors of Christian groups took over the function of the . . . .
26

. . . . The term "bishop" means . . . .
27

An assistant was called a . . . .
28

"The Seven" were . . . .
29

Their function was . . . .
30

The best known men among the Seven are . . . . and
31

. . . .
32

The term "ecclesia" is commonly translated . . . .
33

The early Christian ecclesia was not an organization but a . . . .
34

. . . . In the beginning

of Christianity the only unity which bound together the multiplicity of Christian

groups was the unity of . . . .
35

By the alleged early Christian communism is meant . . . .
36

. . . .

The consideration that prompted this arrangement was the fact that . . . .
37

. . . .

The most noteworthy project for humanitarian relief told about in the

New Testament is the fund raised by . . . . for the relief of
38

. . . . He raised the fund among the
39

. . . .
40

xxv §4. **Number of items adequately stated** = ... × 2½ = Score. . . . .

172

State in what book of the Bible you would look to find each of the following.

1. "All things are lawful for me, but not all things are expedient. All things are lawful for me, but I will not be brought under the power of any. . . . All things are lawful, but not all things are edifying."

  1

2. "Be not overcome by evil, but conquer evil with good."

  2

3. "Christ died for our sins according to the scriptures."

  3

4. "For the kingdom of God is not eating and drinking, but uprightness and peace and joy in the Holy Spirit."

  4

5. "For you have been called to be free, brothers; only use not your liberty as an opportunity for the flesh, but in love serve one another."

  5

6. Hymn of the Incarnate Logos.

  6

7. "Now faith means assurance of things hoped for, a conviction about things not seen."

  7

8. Paul's discussion of marriage.

  8

9. Paul's Hymn in Praise of Love.

  9

10. "Pure religion and undefiled in the sight of God and the Father is this, to care for orphans and widows in their trouble, and to keep oneself stainless from the world (of evil)."

   10

11. The account of the early Christians' experience of the Holy Spirit at Pentecost.

   11

12. The Decalogue.

   12

13. The Hymn of the Suffering Servant.

   13

14. "The Lord, whom ye seek, shall suddenly come to his temple."

   14

15. The Lord's Prayer.

   15

16. The Magnificat.
....16

17. The New Jerusalem.
....17

18. The Nunc Dimittis.
....18

19. The primary historical account of the resurrection of Christ.
....19

20. The Sermon on the Mount.
....20

xxv. **Number of items correctly stated** = ... × 5 = Score...........

Give the information necessary to complete the following account of

THE APOSTLE PAUL

Paul was born in the city of ...., which was in the

province of ...., perhaps about the year ....,
2   3

at any rate when .... was Roman emperor. Paul was a Jew of
4

the Diaspora, which means ....

....
5

He enjoyed the civil status of ....,

which he acquired by ....,
6

a fact which implies that ....
7

....
8

Paul's Jewish name was .... He emphasized his Jewish-
9

ness, stating that he was of the tribe of .... and that as
10

to the Jewish law he was a ...., which was the strictest
11

party of Judaism. Such early Jewish education as he received in his home town

would have been acquired in ....

....
12

.... and may have included the learning of the

.... language. He later studied to be a rabbi, in the city
13

of .... under Rabbi ...., successor
14   15

of the famous liberal Rabbi ....
16

Paul could also speak another language, namely ....,
17

a fact that is attested by ....
18

In his home town Paul was surrounded by Hellenistic culture. Of such influ-

ences which played upon him two are especially noteworthy, (1).............
19

.... and

(2) ....
20

The name Paul means ....;
21

conceivably it may have been bestowed on him as a nickname. He suffered from

certain physical maladies; one of them he referred to as a "................................
...."; another malady affected his

....
23

Paul persecuted Christians because ....
24

....
He witnessed and approved the stoning to death of the first Christian martyr,

.... Concerning his anti-Christian animus he said, "I
25

shut up many of the saints in prison, having received authority from the chief

priests, and when they were put to death, I ....
26

...." He "went to the high priest and

asked of him letters to the synagogues in ....
27

so that if he found any who belonged to the .... he might
28

bring them bound to ...." On that journey occurred Paul's
29

conversion, an account of which is in the book of ....
30

Concerning his conversion Paul said that it pleased God "to reveal his Son to

me, so that I might ....
31

...." Directly following his

conversion Paul was baptized and joined the church at ....
32

Forthwith Paul "went away into ....," which means
33

...., where he doubtless immediately
34

began Christian missionary activity. Then after three years he went up to Jeru-

salem to visit .... and remained with him fifteen days.
35

After that he went to ....,
36

where he worked for the next ten years.

At the end of that time Paul was sought out by ....,
37

who brought him to the city of ...., where they both
38

worked for a whole year. During the famine of 46 A.D. they made a trip to-

gether to .... to carry relief to the needy Christians
39

there.

(*Continued on Sheet 2*)

186

After their return from that relief mission these two apostles were commissioned by the church at .... to go on what is generally called Paul's first missionary journey. On part of this journey they had
38

.... to assist them. The first theatre of their activ-
40

ity on this journey was ...., after which they went to
41

..............................., where they established churches
42

among the gentiles in four principal cities, (1)...........................;
43

(2)............................; (3).............................;
44 45

and (4)......................... An interesting incident which happened
46

on this trip was ....
47

....

....

....

Their work completed, they returned to their home base at ....
38

Paul admitted gentiles into the Christian church without requiring them to

....
48

This led to a controversy with the Christian leaders at ....,
49

notably ...., who held that ....
50 51

....

....

To settle the issue Paul made a trip, at the conclusion of his first missionary

journey, to .... and at a conference there he won
49

his point. The far-reaching significance of Paul's victory in that controversy was

that ....
52

....

Paul's second missionary journey started from the same home base at

.... On this journey he was not accompanied by
38

187

..........................., because they had disagreed over ....

37   53

....

Paul's companion at the outset of his second journey was ....

54

They visited the churches in .... which Paul had founded on

42

his first journey. At .... an energetic young Christian

55

named .... joined Paul and .... They

56   54

were "not allowed by the Holy Spirit to speak the word in ....;

57

they tried to go into ...., but the Spirit of Jesus did not

58

permit them." So they went down to ...., where they were

59

joined by .... They then carried the gospel message to the

60

continent of Europe. The first place evangelized was ....

61

After that Paul visited such cities as .... and

62

.... Eventually he reached ...., where

63   64

he spent two years. An interesting incident which occurred on this second journey

was ....

65

....

....

....

While at .... Paul wrote what is the oldest piece of lit-

64

erature in the New Testament, namely .... Other

66

letters written by Paul from the same place were ....

67

and ...., though one of these may have been written after

68

the second journey was completed. At the end of the two years he spent in

.... Paul traveled by sea via ....

64   69

back to ....

38

On his third missionary journey Paul left .... and

38

traveled along the same route as on his second journey, revisited the churches

of ...., and then went to ...., where

42   70

(Continued on Sheet 3)

188

he remained for three years. Some of his associates in the work there were

(1)...............................; (2)...........................; and
    71   72

(3)........................... For three months he argued in the syna-
              73

gogue, without success in winning converts; thereafter he held discussions daily

in the hall of .... A dramatic incident which hap-
                         74

pened at ...., during Paul's ministry there, was ....
              70   75

....

....

....

While located in .... Paul exchanged letters with the
                          70

Christians at ...., and thus arose the New Testament Epis-
                      76

tles (1)........................... and (2)...........................
          77   78

When his work in .... was all done Paul went to
                          70

...................., where he stayed for three months. During that time
      76

he wrote his Epistle to the .... His object in writing
                                      79

this epistle was ....
                                      80

....

Upon departing from .... Paul went to Jerusalem for
                              76

the purpose of ....
                                  81

....

The day after his arrival he went to the Temple to ....
                                                                  82

....

Some Jews pitched upon Paul because they mistakenly supposed that ....
                                                                            83

....

The incident precipitated a riot, as a result of which Paul was placed under

arrest by ....
                              84

The following day Paul made a speech in defense of himself before the ......

...................., but to no avail. For safety he was placed in the
          85

tower of .... A plot to assassinate Paul was reported by
86

.... Because of this Paul was sent under heavy
87

guard to the procurator .... at ....
88   89

After a hearing before the procurator, Paul was kept in prison for two whole

years because ....
90

....

At the end of that time a new procurator named ....
91

took over the administration of Palestine. When this new procurator wanted

to take Paul back to Jerusalem for trial, Paul appealed to the emperor, which

he had a legal right to do because ....
92

Had Paul not done so, he might have been set at liberty; such was the opinion

of ...., before whom Paul, at the request of the
93

procurator, made a speech in self-defense.

Paul was shipped by sea to Rome. En route a dramatic incident occurred,

namely, ...
94

....

In Rome two years elapsed before his case was considered by the imperial high

court. During those years Paul not only continued to preach, but he also

wrote letters to certain of his churches. Paul's letters to the (1)...............
95

........................; (2)......................................;
96

(3).........................; and (4)...........................
97   98

are commonly called the imprisonment epistles. Paul finally died a martyr. He

was beheaded at the command of ....,
99

probably in the year ....
100

xxvi §6. Number of items adequately stated = Score.........

190

Number each item in the second column to correspond with that word in the first column with which it is correctly associated.

1. Amos	( ) About a runaway slave
2. Benediction	( ) Always found at the opening of a Pauline letter
3. Colossae	
4. Colossians	( ) Bible used by first-century Christians
5. Corinth	( ) Church to which Paul wrote a letter which is not
6. I Corinthians	extant
7. II Corinthians	( ) Contains Paul's classic discourse on immortality
8. Diaspora	
9. Doxology	( ) Contains Paul's Hymn in Praise of Love
10. Epaphras	( ) Epistle in which Paul discusses the cosmic signifi-
11. Epaphroditus	cance of Christ
12. Ephesians	
13. Ephesus	( ) First city in Europe where Paul established a church
14. Galatians	( ) He brought a gift to Paul from the Christians at
15. Gentiles	Philippi
16. Habakkuk	( ) Oldest extant letter of Paul
17. Hagiographa	
18. Isaiah	( ) On "Christian Liberty"
19. Jamnia	( ) Pastoral epistle
20. Jeremiah	( ) Prophet who first said "The righteous shall live by
21. Judaizers	faith"
22. Laodicea	
23. Law	( ) Stands first among the Pauline epistles in the New
24. Macedonia	Testament
25. Philemon	( ) Where Paul wrote Romans
26. Philippi	
27. Philippians	( ) Where the final limits of the Jewish canon of Holy
28. Prophets	Scripture were fixed in 90 A.D.
29. Proselytes	( ) Written by Paul during his imprisonment
30. Psalms	( ) Written by Paul on his second missionary journey
31. Romans	
32. Salutation	( ) Written by Paul on his third missionary journey
33. Septuagint	( ) Written by Paul to a church he didn't found
34. Thanksgiving	
35. I Thessalonians	
36. II Thessalonians	
37. I Timothy	
38. II Timothy	
39. Titus	
40. Torah	

xxvii §1.   Number of items correctly numbered = ... × 5 = Score........

Give the information necessary to complete the following statements.

1. Three sources which shaped the thought and style of the New Testament Epistle of James were:

   (1)...

   ....

   (2)...

   ....

   (3)...

   ....

2. The New Testament book of .... reflects the Hellenistic philosophy associated with the city of .... and with the Jewish philosopher ....

3. "The Apocalypse of Jesus Christ" is otherwise known as the book of ......
   ....

4. I Peter reflects a situation of persecution of Christians in the area of
   ....

   The reason why they were being persecuted was that ....

   ....

   The basic aim of I Peter was to ....

   ....

5. New Testament books which were directed against heresy are ....

   ....

   The types of heresy opposed in these books are:

   (1) Docetism, which affirmed that ....

   ....

   (2) Gnosticism, which affirmed that ....

   ....

   (3) Libertinism, which affirmed that ....

   ....

   (4) Perfectionism, which affirmed that ....

   ....

6. The author of the book of Revelation was ....

7. The New Testament book of .... portrays Christ as a compassionate high priest, faithful in the service of God.

8. To "fear God" and "honor the king" is advised in the book of ....
   ....

9. The "Vision of the New Jerusalem" is in the book of ....

10. Two New Testament epistles which are very much alike, that is, have much
    in common, are (1).................... and (2)...................

11. By a pseudepigraph is meant ....
    ....
    An example among New Testament books is ....

xxvii §§2–4. Number of items adequately stated = ... × 4 = Score.......

194

Who or what were the following?

1. Athanasius: ....
   ....

2. Barnabas: ....
   ....

3. Canon: ....
   ....

4. Clement: ....
   ....

5. Codex: ....
   ....

6. Cursive: ....
   ....

7. Eusebius: ....
   ....

8. Hermas: ....
   ....

9. Jerome: ....
   ....

10. Laodiceans: ....
    ....

11. Marcion: ....
    ....

12. Muratori: ....
    ....

13. Origen: ....
    ....

14. Pandect: ....
    ....

15. Papyrus: ....
    ....

16. Sinaiticus: ....
    ....

17. Tischendorf: ....
    ....

18. Uncial: ....
....

19. Vaticanus: ....
....

20. Vulgate: ....
....

xxvii §§5–6. **Number of adequate statements** = ... $\times$ 5 = **Score**........

196

Indicate whether the following statements are true or false by underscoring the appropriate word. Correct any false statement on the blank line following it; the first half of any statement must be retained in any proposed correction.

1. St. Jerome made the translation of the Bible which is known as / the Septuagint.

   . . . .   TRUE   FALSE   1

2. St. Jerome's translation of the Bible was completed / at the beginning of the fifth century A.D.

   . . . .   TRUE   FALSE   2

3. The official Bible of the Roman Catholic Church is / the Vulgate.

   . . . .   TRUE   FALSE   3

4. The official English Bible of the Roman Catholic Church is / the Douay Version.

   . . . .   TRUE   FALSE   4

5. The so-called Authorized Version means / the King James Bible.

   . . . .   TRUE   FALSE   5

6. The Venerable Bede translated / the four gospels into Anglo-Saxon in 735 A.D.

   . . . .   TRUE   FALSE   6

7. The first translation of the Bible into English was made / in 1382.

   . . . .   TRUE   FALSE   7

8. The first English translation of the Bible was made from / the Septuagint.

   . . . .   TRUE   FALSE   8

9. The first Bible ever printed was / the Wyclif English Version.

   . . . .   TRUE   FALSE   9

10. The Wyclif translation was made from / the Latin.   TRUE   FALSE   10

    . . . .

11. The first Greek New Testament ever printed was prepared by / John Gutenberg.

    . . . .   TRUE   FALSE   11

12. The Coverdale Bible was published / before the Tyndale Bible.

    . . . .   TRUE   FALSE   12

13. The Myles Coverdale Bible was / his own translation from the original languages.   TRUE   FALSE   13

. . . .

14. Wm. Tyndale's English New Testament was published / in 1525.   TRUE   FALSE   14

. . . .

15. Just prior to his death, Wm. Tyndale completed the translation of / the entire Bible from the original languages.   TRUE   FALSE   15

. . . .

16. The John Rogers Bible is / the same as the Thomas Cromwell Bible.   TRUE   FALSE   16

. . . .

17. The first English Bible "appointed to be read in the Churches" was / the Great Bible.   TRUE   FALSE   17

. . . .

18. The Great Bible / supplanted the Bishop's Bible.   TRUE   FALSE   18

. . . .

19. The first English Bible to contain the division of chapters into verses was / the Geneva Bible.   TRUE   FALSE   19

. . . .

20. The King James Bible was published / in 1609.   TRUE   FALSE   20

. . . .

21. The greatness of the King James Bible is due to the genius of / Wm. Tyndale.   TRUE   FALSE   21

. . . .

22. The Bible brought to America by the early English settlers was / the Geneva Bible.   TRUE   FALSE   22

. . . .

23. The Revised Version of the English Bible was published / in 1881.   TRUE   FALSE   23

. . . .

24. The Revised Standard Version of the New Testament was published / in 1946.   TRUE   FALSE   24

. . . .

25. "The Complete Bible, An American Translation" means / the American Standard Version.   TRUE   FALSE   25

. . . .

xxvii §7. Number of statements correctly judged and adequately corrected = ...

× 4 = Score . . . . . .

APPENDIX

PROJECTS AND TOPICS

For investigation, class reports, or short papers

I

On a map of Palestine superimpose a map of that part of the United States in which you live, *drawn to the same scale,* and in a different color of ink, spotting your home town upon the site of Jerusalem. Trace the highways or railroads that lead from your home town and observe the districts and towns of Palestine you would pass through along them, and note just where you would be when you came to the boundary of Palestine.

II

Genesis 10:21 states that Shem was "the father of all the children of Eber." Who were the children of Eber? What does "Eber" mean?

The Jacob-Esau stories show that the Hebrews regarded the Edomites as about the closest of their kinsmen. How?

Write on "The Habiri."

III

What is meant by the term monument as used in biblical archaeology? Give examples of various types of monuments.

Write on the languages in use, the styles of writing, and writing materials employed in the ancient biblical world.

Prepare a paper on the discovery, contents, and significance of the Rosetta Stone.

Prepare a paper on the discovery, contents, and significance of the Behistun Inscription.

Prepare a paper on archaeological research in Palestine in the last ten years.

IV

Read I Samuel 13:19–22 in the American Standard Version, and then read it in *The Bible, An American Translation* (the Chicago version), and then write an interpretation of it, pointing out its cultural implications.

V

Write a paragraph that will make as vividly picturesque as possible the expression, "While shepherds watched their flocks by night."

Write on "The Status of Woman in Nomadic Hebrew Society."

Write on "Community Social Life in the Nomadic Period."

Write on "The Economic Status of the Average Hebrew in the Nomadic Era."

VI

Write on "Egypt under Ramses II."

Discuss the effects of life in Egypt on the Hebrews.

Discuss "The Red Sea."

Interpret the expression, "The waters were a wall unto them" (Exodus 14:22), which is used in connection with the crossing of the Red Sea.

Discuss pro and con the location of Mount Sinai.

Trace (either by sketch map or descriptive paragraph) the route of the exodus and the wilderness wandering. Identify the more important places. Explain why they went the way they did.

Prepare a paper on the social progress made by the Hebrews during the time that intervened between their departure from Egypt and their entrance into Palestine.

VII

Write a critical appraisal of the literary characteristics of "My Favorite Story in Genesis."

Discuss and illustrate the statement: "The antecedents of Hebrew literature lie in the social experience of the people of nomadic days."

Discuss the statement: "The only art which characterized the Hebrews in the nomadic period was the art of poetry and story-telling; it was in the very psychology of the race."

Discuss the communal character of folklore.

Point out the literary structure of Numbers 10:35–36, and explain its historical and religious significance.

VIII

Discuss the statement: "Their religion defines the level of culture which the Hebrews attained."

Read Genesis 35:20 and discuss the significance of the Pillar of Rachel's Grave.

Read Exodus 8:26 and explain the significance of the Egyptians stoning Hebrews for sacrificing.

Read Numbers 21:6–8 and discuss the significance of the brazen serpent.

What is implied in such a reference as that in Deuteronomy 33:16 to Yahweh as "him that dwelt in the bush"?

Read Judges 5:4–5 and discuss what it implies as to the nature of Yahweh.

Interpret Exodus 19.

IX

Interpret Judges 9.

Interpret Judges 18.

"It is important to bear in mind the cultural contrast between the Canaanites and the invading Hebrews." Discuss the contrast.

Justify the statement: "Gideon, in repelling the Midianites, was fighting the battle of the older inhabitants of Canaan as much as of the Hebrews themselves, which fact no doubt contributed to the fusion of Canaanites and Hebrews."

"In those days there was no king in Israel; every man did that which was right in his own eyes." Discuss the social situation this implies.

Explain the statement: "Two peoples, the Philistines and the Hebrews, were both at the same time seeking to gain the control of the same land."

Report on "The Canaanites and their Fate."

Write on "Community Social Life in the Judges Period."

Write on "The Economic Status of the Average Hebrew in the Judges Period."

X

Expound: "Yahweh is a man of war." (Exodus 15:3).

Prepare a report on the appointments (equipment) of a high place.

Report on the nature of the worship of Ashtart, the mother-goddess.

How did Yahweh come to be regarded as a god controlling agriculture?

Discuss the statement: "Baalism went hand in hand with village patriotism."

Discuss the statement: "Yahwism was basic to the Hebrew national unity that was desired by reason of the Philistine menace."

XI

With what states did Solomon make political marriages, and locate each such state with respect to Hebrew territory.

Outline the military and administrative organization of the Hebrew kingdom in the time of David and Solomon.

Discuss: "Solomon engaged in extensive commercial enterprises that brought in wealth." Report on the light on this matter which has been shed by the recent archaeological excavation of Ezion-Geber.

Describe "Jerusalem's Earliest History and its Founding as the National Capital of the Hebrews."

XII

Prepare a paper on Kings David and Solomon as Patrons of Literature.

XIII

Interpret the expression: "The sin which Jeroboam sinned, and wherewith he made all Israel to sin."

Write on "The Causes and Consequences of the Hebrew National Schism."

Write on "The Gains and Losses of the Disruption of the United Hebrew Kingdom."

XIV

Report on "Assyrian Political Policy and its Bearing on the Hebrew Kingdoms."

Prepare a paper on "Prophets and Politics."

Write on "The Peril of Prosperity."

XV

Imagine yourself a thoughtful Hebrew living somewhere in Palestine in the year 720 B.C. What reflections would occupy your mind?

Imagine yourself a thoughtful Jew living in Judah in the year 700 B.C. What do you think about national and international affairs?

Imagine yourself as being a Hebrew prophet living in Jerusalem in 650 B.C. Write out a prophecy of about 250 words such as might give your interpretation of the times and a message to your contemporaries.

XVI

Imagine yourself a thoughtful Jew living in the year 580 B.C. What reflections would occupy your mind?

XVII

Write on "The Most Interesting Development in Hebrew Literature Prior to 586 B.C."

Make a careful comparison of Genesis 16:1-2, 4-14 and Genesis 21:6-21. What revealing differences do you detect in the authors' background? Which tale is more true to life? Why?

Write on "Individualism versus Social Solidarity in Hebrew Thought."

Write on "The Origin and Nature of the Hebrew Aristocracy."

XVIII

Interpret Isaiah 6.

Prepare a paper on "The Evolution of the Idea of God in Hebrew Religion Prior to 586 B.C."

Prepare a paper on "The Evolution of the Ethical in Hebrew Religion."

XIX

Expound each of the following statements:

"The Hebrew exiles in Babylonia experienced there a profound social transformation."

"Cyrus reversed the policy of previous conquerors in dealing with exiles."

"In Babylonia the Hebrew exiles developed into a literary people, and their religion into a religion of 'The Book.' "

' In Babylonia the Jews cast off the outworn shell of Judean provincialism and became a cosmopolitan people."

"The disorder attending the accession of Darius I evidently fanned the flame of hope among the Jews of Judea that once again they might set up an independent kingdom."

"The exilic period witnessed a marked impulse toward hymnology."

Prepare a paper on "Exiles and Refugees—the Beginnings of the Diaspora."

XX

Explain the statement: "Short as was Alexander's reign, within that period he planned and set in motion a vast ambitious Hellenizing program which was to go on, long after his death, with little loss of momentum, and to become one of the most remarkable examples of acculturization that the world had ever witnessed."

Prepare a paper on "Post-exilic Judaism."

Write on "The Economic Status of the Plain Man of Judea under Late Persian and Early Greek Rule."

XXI

Prepare a paper on "How Jewish Freedom was Gained and Forfeited."

Write on "Hellenism and Antisemitism."

XXII

Prepare a paper on "What Jews were Thinking and Writing in the Second and First Centuries Before Christ."

Prepare a paper on "The Development of the Old Testament as a Body of Sacred Literature."

XXIII

Imagine yourself a Jew in Palestine in the first century A.D. Write a letter to a relative in the Diaspora telling about conditions in the homeland.

XXIV

Prepare a paper on "When Jesus was as Old as I am." Include a discussion of what was going on in Palestine, and especially in Galilee; the political factions and religious sects bidding for his allegiance; and his own personal activities.

XXV

Imagine yourself as attending a Christian group meeting about the middle of the first century A.D. Describe what took place and the impressions it made upon you.

Imagine yourself a thoughtful Gentile, not a Christian, living somewhere in the Mediterranean world about the middle of the first century A.D. and becoming converted to Christianity. What religious interests and connections did you have before you learned about Christianity? How did you find out about Christianity? What induced you to become a Christian?

XXVI

Imagine that you were the Apostle Paul visiting for the first time the synagogue in some city in the North Mediterranean World where you had not previously been and being invited to address the congregation. Compose a five-minute address appropriate to such an occasion, a synthetic address made up of verses or ideas taken here and there from Paul's writings such as will state the essence of Paul's gospel message.

Compose an "Epistle of Paul the Apostle to the Antiochians," such as Paul might appropriately have written when he was a prisoner at Rome.

On an outline map of the North Mediterranean World trace the routes of Paul's journeys.

Write on "How they Brought the Good News to Egypt."

XXVII

Write on "E Pluribus Unum—How Many Books Became One Bible."